Major VARIETY - ODDITY Guide

of

UNITED STATES COINS

4th EDITION

By F. G. SPADONE

LISTING ALL U. S. COINS FROM

HALF CENTS THROUGH GOLD COINS

FULLY ILLUSTRATED, WITH VALUES

CONTAINS TECHNICAL DATA FROM SURVEYS AND YEARS OF RESEARCH, ESTIMATES OF QUANTITY KNOWN, AND RARITIES.

Copyright MCMLXVII

KRAUSE PUBLICATIONS, INC.

IOLA, WISCONSIN 54945 • U.S.A.

Library of Congress Catalogue Card No. 67-18968

Anderson Import-Export Co., Florence, Alabama
Exclusive Distributors

1

FOREWORD

The author welcomes you to hours of enjoyment that can be yours through use of this fourth edition of the Major Variety-Oddity Guide. The purpose of this book is to be of service to the hobby, and in it we have endeavored to be as accurate as possible. There may be room for improvement, and we will welcome your ideas and suggestions for the bettering of future editions. Letters, photos and inquiries are welcome; if you wish an answer, please enclose a stamped, self-addressed envelope.

The prices shown here have been determined through reference to auction sales, advertisements, and dealer and contributor experience. In addition to these printed price references, we make available a limited service in the examining, attributing and appraising of new finds and oddities. If you send in your special find, please enclose $3 to cover our small service charge and return postage, handling and insurance.

For the sake of simplicity, the mintages shown have been rounded off to the last three digits. Since many coins are lost, mutilated, destroyed and otherwise banished from view, it is safe to say that the coins actually in circulation are fewer than the mintages shown.

The collecting of mint errors has become an increasingly popular field within the coin hobby. It has attracted thousands of new enthusiasts and established a need for its own specialized coin clubs, publications and market supplies. This book contains a listing of clubs you may join and mint error publications you may subscribe to; they are good media to help you buy and sell your coins. The author does not solicit to buy or sell any items listed.

This book is on sale nationwide and in some foreign markets. Our leading distributors supply some 3,000 coin-stamp book stores. If you find the book unavailable in your area, write to us and we will help you.

It is possible that you may not find every one of your specific finds listed here. We have limited new find listings in the "filled die" and "cracked die" categories. A study of the two categories shows that there could be literally thousands of these minor oddities to be listed, the majority of them virtually the same except for size and location of the oddity. To list them all would require several large volumes. We have, however, listed all the important and popular oddities.

A feature of this guide is the code index for classifying every date and its varieties. The code will help collectors and advertisers to list and recognize specific dates and types of oddities. It also will allow future entries to be readily listed and located. The index column on the far left margin of the pages lists the code number for every date and a small letter for each variety of that date. Thus, the book's first listing, S1, is the 1793 half cent, S2 is the 1794 half cent, and S2a is the 1794 half cent divided date variety. The S stands for Spadone.

2

What is a given variety or oddity worth? There is no pat answer to this often-asked question. There are no fixed prices in the variety-oddity field; the law of supply and demand prevails. Thus, any specific coin or variety is worth what someone is willing to pay for it at the time you want to sell it. Eventually we can expect the give and take of the market to evolve some standard values, but this is a comparatively new field of collecting and it will take time.

Even so, there are a few areas in which approximate values can be cited. Interesting examples of overlooked varieties that bring fabulous prices are the overdates on which one or more numbers have been repunched or recut. The 1918/7-D nickel sold for less than $35 in 1954 and today it sells for over $1,500. I recall buying the 1942/1 dime at $8 in XF, and at $18 uncirculated; today it brings over $300 uncirculated. Another variety is the 1955 double die shift cent which used to sell for 50 cents and now brings over $250. Other cent varieties include the 1960 double D mint mark, the 1961-D over horizontal D, and the 1960 small date. The latter when first discovered was ignored by many, but it now brings $8 or more. A five cent variety often found in circulation and now bringing a premium is the 1938-D/S buffalo nickel.

Beyond these are many other items, considered minor oddities, which once sold for a few cents and now bring premiums of several dollars each. The law of supply and demand is making itself felt.

In time we can expect the common accumulation method of collecting to give way more and more to specialized collecting. Some of the categories already proving popular with specialists are double mint marks, Liberty (BIE), overdates, double struck coins and off center pieces.

Commercial supplies for the oddity-variety collector are always open to improvement. Perhaps you have procedures that would help, such as a unique method of housing your coins or an unusual system of collecting. We would like to hear from you so we can serve you better.

This guide was originated in response to growing collector interest. While varieties and oddities have existed for centuries, this phase of coin collecting waited until recent years to come into its own with a tremendous rise in popularity. Today it provides a fascinating challenge to thousands of collectors seeking new and often valuable pieces among our millions of circulated coins. It has opened new avenues of pleasure and excitement in the numismatic field.

The essence of a hobby is enjoyment of the undertaking and a sharing of that enjoyment with others. Knowledge and fulfillment are the goals. So collect for fun and enjoyment, the profit will take care of itself. And happy hunting to you.

F. G. Spadone

ACKNOWLEDGMENTS

The author would like to thank the many who have contributed with their letters and comments. My thanks and appreciation to Chief Engraver of the United States Mint, Mr. Gilroy Roberts, for the past courtesy and patience in answering and explaining inquiries.

A special thanks to Charles Lotcpeich, Q. David Bowers, James S. Ruddy, Zedell Jackson, I. K. Stevenson, J. W. Scott, Irving Swalwell and Nick Salimbene for the use of information, photos, listings, and rare coins from their collection and stock.

To the following who have contributed with information, values, advice and listings, and to the many hundreds not listed who have also helped in one way or another, many thanks.   F. G. Spadone

John Agugliaro
Rev. R.B. Anderson
Joe Angello
Bill Atkinson
D. Banulski
J.D. Barker
Karl W. Bathmann
George Behen
W.E. Bench
Milton Berel
Dr. Conway Bolt
Donald Brigandi
John E. Brown
Robert S. Brown
Robert L. Brownell
H. Burbach
Joseph Bush
O.C. Caldren
James Caldwell
Ruby L. Caplinger
Jean Caraway
Dr. Theodore Carlton
Dr. David Caul
David Church
Richard A. Church
Jules Cigelski
John J. Cinikas
H. Cohen
B. Collard
Sgt. R.W. Cooper
Alan Craig
Michael Danish
Paul H. Davis
R. Dennis
A.M. De Palma
Pasquale Di Capra
C.J. Dockhus
David Echols
Ralph Ecton
Frederick J. Egger
Stanley Elkins
Jack Fiorino
H.C. Fischer
Leonard Puffer
William Fivaz
Robert Fleming
Joseph Flemming
Phillip Florio
Armand Forman
Martin Forrest
George Fowler
John P. Freeman
Dr. H. Friedman

G. Geiger
Jack Gengler
Peter Georgis
Harry Gerlach
Ray Gold
Edwin Golinski
Gale Good
Maurice M. Gould
Larry Grabert
Stanley Grzybowski
Charles Haas
William Heines
Dr. C.A. Herbin
Lee Hewitt
B. Hilton
David J. Hines
Dr. Charles Hoffman
J.C. Holman
R.H. Hoover
Mrs. Ruth Houshoulder
W.H. Hughes
R.C. Huntley
M. Inglesino
James G. Johnson
Alex Kapp
Louis Karp
Frank Kasprowski
Donald Keys
David Kimbrough
Elmer Kirk
Ray Knight
Albert Kramer
Chester Krause
L.A. Larson
Raymond L. Larson
Adolph Lippke
Teresa Luimento
Kaniel Lutzky
Albert Magilo
Thomas J. Mangan
Philip Martin
Peggy Massey
Capt. E. McBrayer
George McGrath
E. Michalski
Ralph Miele
Edward Milchak
William Mincher
Dr. Ronald Moreschini
Paul Mulvilill
J. Murphy
Earl W. Neely
John C. Negretti

Dr. Harry Neustadt
J.R. Newman
Edward Obrycki
Phillip O'Hara
(Peachy) Olympia
Dr. S. Ostrowski
George Packard
James Paradis
A. Pfeiffer
Rev. J. Popovich
Leonard Puffer
Norman Pullen
Brian Richards
Ken Rimondi
Robert Rizzolo
Frank S. Robinson
Glenn E. Rodgers
Ralph R. Rosati
Roaul Rose
Phillip Rosenbaum
Joe Rosenfield, Jr.
Reginald Ruxten
Anthony Scarpone
C. Schaub
Paul W. Scherf
A.F. Schieber
John Shue
H. Silberman
Joe S. Simon
Leonard Sless
Arthur Smith
Denver Smith
Frank F. Smith
Prof. Henry G. Smith
R. Bynum Smith
John G. Spadone
Ernest L. Spigelmire
Harris Strong
Mary Thomas
Ralph Ugaro
Ed. Vaskas
R. Van Wagner
Marshall H. Ward, III
Harry Warshaw
Paul Whitehead
Robert Wilson
William Wolfson (M.D.)
Fred Wong
George Woods
C.E. Wycech
Martin Young
Al Conti

How Varieties or Oddities Come About

The new collector no doubt would like to know how the many types of varieties and oddities originate. Also, under what classification would they be assembled. The following listing shows categories, and how the coins are attributed.

FILLED DIES A blank or missing part of the date, lettering or design is caused by metal filings, or foreign matter. These particles clog the incused area, thus when the die strikes the blank it leaves a missing portion.

CRACKED DIES Are due to over working, foreign matter, or improper annealling which can cause brittle metal. A chip or crack in a die will leave a corresponding raised mark on the coin. Both the obverse and reverse dies have the designs, lettering and dates incused. When the die strikes the blank planchet the metal is forced into the incused parts and raised, similar to moulding.

CLASH DIES Exactly as stated, both dies strike each other without a blank planchet between them. Depending on the sharpness of the incused designs and the metal temperament, one or both dies will have a raised outline of the other's design. Since this is cut into the die metal and leaves a permanent cut, the result will appear on many coins until it is worn out. The procedure is similar to Cracked Dies as above. What may appear as a cracked die variety or a scratched surface, under a strong glass will prove to be a clash die variety.

OFF METAL This means the coin was struck in a metal other than the intended. For example, a cent design struck on a dime planchet, a nickel struck with a quarter design. This off metal type occurs when blanks remain in the hopper when the dies are changed to a different denomination. This error can cause different denomination sizes also.

DOTS A dot is sometimes placed on dies to help identify them. For example a half cent has them on the reverse side, some Morgan silver dollars have them on the reverse side on the left bow of ribbon, and near the designer's initial near the neck hair curl. The 1884 dollar is noted for many of these dots.

OVERDATES This variety is the result of one or more digits of the date being re-engraved or repunched with a later date number. The reason for this procedure is the time and cost of engraving a new die. In case of a rush for more coins, time is saved by punching a new digit on the date instead of producing a new die. During the early days of minting, when costs were high, this method helped conserve expenses.

DOUBLE MINT MARKS The double impression is caused by the punch die bouncing when struck. This could be from the engraver's hand, or the die being brittle. In some cases double mint marks are known to be of different mints (D/S). Since the mint mark is punched by hand, the position can vary on different dies. Some double mint marks are known to have horizontal positions, with corrections made with a regular upright punch. For example the 1961 D over horizontal D Cent, 1942 D over horizontal D nickel, and the 1938 D over S Buffalo nickel.

MICRO DOUBLE SHIFT This variety is known on many coins, and any part of the coin could appear doubled. Actually this is the result of "out of level dies" which create an excess of metal flow. When two dies are not level parallel to each other, one edge of both dies will meet before the opposite edge. To create an even, proper impress on the whole surface of the coin, the press depth pressure is made greater. The dies might only be off a few thousandths of an inch to cause a metal flow. The difference between micro shift and double die shift is that the latter's doubling is spaced apart while the former appears almost the same but not spaced.

DOUBLE DIE SHIFT is illustrated by the 1955 Double Die cent. The 1934 P quarter is also known to have a double die shift. This rare variety is caused when the master hub impression is being made on a blank working die. The master hub has the features intaglio (raised or protruding) and the impression is punched into the soft blank die. Should the die shift slightly with this operation, a double impression is made on the working die. This die will then transfer the double impression onto the blank planchets.

ROTATED DIES If you hold a coin between your fingers upright and slowly turn it around, you will note the obverse-reverse designs are upside down from each other. This is the normal standard, however some coins have been found to have both sides upright, or one design rotated from 5 to 300 degrees. This is the result of either die being loose, thus the varying degree of rotation. The bottom die, the reverse design, is more likely to cause this error, for this die is stationary. A loose lock screw will cause the die to shift or vibrate. The upper obverse die is also locked in place with a lock screw, however its not possible for this die to move more than a few degrees if the screw is loose; beyond this the die would fall out of the press.

GENERAL PRIMER

A BRIEFING IN GENERAL ON HOW COIN ERRORS ARE MADE

SMELTING-STRIPS Metal alloys are melted and poured into ingots, ready to be rolled into strips ready for blanking. During the period of cooling the molten ingots, if any foreign matter or air is trapped it can cause a coin's surface to peel, appear laminated or have tiny crevices. The ingots are put through rollers several times to reduce the thickness to a given standard; for example, a cent blank is approximately .047 thick. With the upset rim edge (finished product) .061.

BLANKING The finished strips are approximately 5 inches wide and 35 feet long. These strips are fed into multiple die blanks in an operation that will produce about 2,000 blanks per strip. The perforated strip is then salvaged for remelting for more ingots. The errors may now occur if an uneven edge of the strip is punched out. The edge could be diagonally or otherwised shaped, thus a finished coin with an odd edge could be found in circulation.

CLIPPED PLANCHETS When the blanks are being punched out during this fast operation, some blanks may not eject properly, creating a jam. The multiple dies will over-strike two or more blanks and create clips of various sizes. Some blanks could receive several clips.

UPSETTING EDGES The blanks are then conveyed through the roller upset machine. This process rolls the edge of the blank by pressure at the sides, and causes the rim to raise slightly higher than the flat blank surface. This upsetting protects the coin's surface for better circulation wear; it also allows for proper pressure expansion in the collar during the striking.

STRIKING OBVERSE-REVERSE The finished blanks are now fed to the dies by a storage hopper. The blanks rest on the stationary lower die (reverse design) and are struck by the upper punch die (obverse). Both impressions are made in the same stroke. Should a faulty mechanism fail to eject the coin properly, a double impression or an off-centered struck blank would result. Should a coin already struck fail to eject and an oncoming blank rest over it, the extended pressure created by two coins in the collar would cause the obverse of the bottom coin to smear and appear larger. The reverse side of the bottom coin would not be affected. There are a number of error combinations that can result from defective mechanisms. Considering that thousands of coins are struck at high speed, a number of defects can occur. File scraps and foreign particles can fill the tiny incused parts of the die design. This will cause a "filled die variety," a partial or complete missing digit, lettering or design.

An overworked or defective die could crack or chip. The fault will leave crevices (incuse), and when struck against a blank will leave a raised impression, such as a dot, thin or heavy line, or any odd design. The finished coin is then counted, bagged and stored, ready for shipment to the Federal Reserve banks, which then distribute to local banks for general circulation.

FINAL WORD To attribute newly found errors, a study of the above chapter will help a great deal in identifying the type phase error.

EDGES

MILLED •PLAIN• LETTERED • OBLIQUE REEDED •ORNAMENTED •ENGRAILED •VINE• BARS

BORDERS

BEADED ∞∞∞∞∞ SERRATED⋀⋀⋀⋀ OR⋀⋀⋀⋀ AND⋀⋀⋀⋀ ORNAMENTED⋅∞∞∞∞∞

Various Abbreviations Used To Describe A Coin

Pf.—Proof
B. U. —Bright Unc.
Unc.—Uncirculated
X. F. —Extra Fine
Brill.—Brilliant
G.-V.G.—Good to Very Good
G./V.G.—Obverse Good, Reverse Very Good
C. V. —Catalog Value
Var.—Variety
Dupl.—Duplicate
Avg.—Average
Mm.—Millimeter
Scf.—Scuffed
Scr.—Scratched
Ctspd.—Counterstamped
R.—Right

L.—Left
AU.—Gold
Ag.—Silver
L. L. —Large Letters
S. L. —Small Letters
AE—Minor
Coll.—Collection
Comm.—Commemorative
MM—Mint Mark
Lib.—Liberty
Hd.—Head
Unique—one only
Bt.—Bust
Laur.—Laureate
42/41—Overdate
Crd.—Crowned
Diad.—Diademed

N. D. —No Date
Obv.—Obverse
Rev.—Reverse
W.—With, Within
Wr.—Wreath
Ins.—Inscription
F. E. —Flying Eagle
W. C. —With Cents
N. C. —No Cents
C. N.— Copper Nickel
P.O.R.—Price On Request
T., Ty.—Type
Sm.—Small
Lg.—Large
Stg.—Standing
Std.—Seated

GRADING STANDARD

PROOF—Coin has a mirror-like finish, especially struck for collectors on polished metal blanks and struck by slower hydraulic press to obtain best feature lines.

UNCIRCULATED—Made for general circulation. A Gem is well struck, has lustre, no scratches, rubbing or mars.

EXTRA FINE & A. U.—About same. Coin about uncirculated is slightly worn on high points and may have some mint lustre.

V.FINE—Has been circulated but all features and lettering are sharp.

FINE—Has all features and lettering but not sharp. Liberty is readable.

V.G.—Has border, rims, most features and lines visible. Part of Liberty visible.

GOOD—All features and lines worn but visible.

FAIR—Considerably worn.

POOR—Almost worn smooth, or corroded, good only as space filler.

8

DOUBLE MINT MARK GUIDE CHART

The double mint marks are the result of the same process as the popular 1955 double die shift cent. The reason for double shifts occurring is that the die receiving the impression transfer was not properly annealed (softened). A brittle or case hardened die could cause the die to bounce when it receives the transfer blow, thus leaving a double or multiple impression.

In some cases part of the multiple impression could be weak or the die filled, creating a partial letter such as a broken D appearing as an L, I, or C. Thus we have D/C, D/L, and DD/C.

Double mint marks, whether from San Francisco, Denver or New Orleans, are brothers to the double die shift cent, and the only difference is that the proportionate amount doubled is not as great. A series of double mint marks can make an interesting set. Such a collection can be inexpensive yet has a great future potential both in popularity and value.

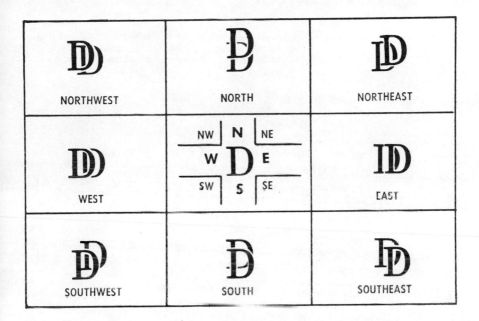

NORTHWEST	NORTH	NORTHEAST
WEST		EAST
SOUTHWEST	SOUTH	SOUTHEAST

VARIOUS DOUBLE PARTIAL MINT MARKS

The last heavy impression would be the shift direction. Double mint marks with both full impressions opposite each other are called perfect parallel, and are the most popular.

Micro double (microscopic) shift is not the same as above.

The shift is not separate — yet has the appearance of being double because of "out of level" die pressure.

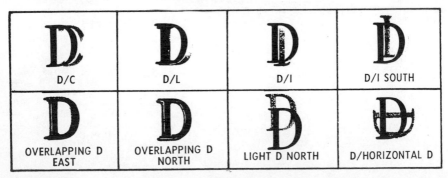

| D/C | D/L | D/I | D/I SOUTH |
| OVERLAPPING D EAST | OVERLAPPING D NORTH | LIGHT D NORTH | D/HORIZONTAL D |

HALF CENTS 1793 - 1857

Index #	Date	Description	Mintage	Good	Fine	Unc.

The half cent is the smallest denomination issued by the U.S., the reverse contains the fraction 1/200, with the early issues having the edge lettered. All half cents are scarce, especially in choice condition.

Due to the lack of the present day modern machinery and techniques early half and large cents contain weak strikes in various positions. The few that are well struck and with little or no wear are rare. Grading of early U.S. copper half and large cents isn't the same as a modern coin. Uncirculated and proofs are extremely rare.

Index #	Date	Description	Mintage	Good	Fine	Unc.
S1	1793	head of liberty facing left	—	255.00	690.00	—
S2	1794		81,600	60.00	150.00	—
a	1794	divided date (1 79 4)	—	65.00	160.00	—
S3	1795		25,600	55.00	145.00	—
a	1795	struck on cut down Talbert-Lee Colonial cents	—	55.00	145.00	—
b	1795	plain edge no pole	—	55.00	145.00	—
c	1795	lettered edge, pole	—	55.00	145.00	—
d	1795	lettered edge punct. date	—	65.00	150.00	—
e	1795	plain edge punct. date	—	65.00	150.00	—
S4	1796	very rare	—			
		(most were melted or lost)		1200.00	2800.00	—
a	1796	plain edge, pole	115,400	1200.00	2800.00	—
b	1796	plain edge, no pole	—	1300.00	2900.00	—
S5	1797	also on cut down cents	107,000	50.00	150.00	—
a	1797	1 over 1 in date plain edge	—	55.00	135.00	—
b	1797	lettered edge	—	110.00	650.00	—

BUST TYPE

Index #	Date	Description	Mintage	Good	Fine	Unc.
S6	1800		211,500	12.50	35.00	—
S7	1802	all struck/1800	14,360	85.00	210.00	—
a	1802	reverse of 1800	—	250.00	575.00	—
S8	1803		97,900	9.00	30.00	—
S9	1804		1,055,000	8.50	16.00	75.00
a	1804	plain 4, stemless rev.	—	8.50	16.00	75.00
b	1804	plain 4, stems on rev.	—	22.50	50.00	—
c	1804	crosslet 4, stemless rev.	—	12.00	26.00	90.00
d	1804	crosslet 4, stems rev.	—	11.00	18.00	75.00
e	1804	spiked chin	—	12.00	26.50	95.00
f	1804	double struck, obv.	—	—	75.00	—
S10	1805		814,000	10.00	21.00	95.00
a	1805	small 5, stemless rev.	—	10.00	21.00	95.00
b	1805	small 5, stems rev.	—	46.50	165.00	—
c	1805	large 5, stems	—	11.00	20.00	—
d	1805	double profile	—	25.00	80.00	—
S11	1806		356,000	9.00	20.00	75.00
a	1806	small 6, stems	—	28.00	70.00	—
b	1806	small 6, stemless	—	9.00	20.00	90.00
c	1806	large 6, stems	—	9.00	20.00	90.00
S12	1807		476,000	9.00	16.00	—
S13	1808		400,000	8.50	16.00	—
a	1808/7	overdate	—	45.00	95.00	400.00

HALF CENTS

Index #	Date	Description	Mintage	Good	Fine	Unc.
TURBAN HEAD TYPE						
S14	1809	....	1,154,000	9.00	16.00	75.00
a	1809	filled date die (−09).............	—	15.00	26.00	95.00
b	1809	wide date	—	9.00	17.00	80.00
c	1809/6	over date............................	—	12.50	22.00	90.00
d	1809	circle inside of O	—	9.50	19.00	80.00
S15	1810		215,000	9.50	26.00	175.00

**1811 RESTRIKE
OBVERSE AND REVERSE
(6 STRUCK, 4 KNOWN)**

Index #	Date	Description	Mintage	Good	Fine	Unc.
S16	1811	....	63,150	48.00	90.00	550.00
a	1811	restrike rev. of 1802	6	—	—	—
S17	1825	....	63,000	7.50	14.00	75.00
S18	1826	....	234,000	7.50	14.00	75.00
S19	1828	13 stars...........................	606,000	7.00	10.00	65.00
a	1828	12 stars...........................	—	9.50	22.00	95.00
S20	1829	....	487,000	7.00	12.00	70.00
S21	1831	(known in proofs only)	2,200	—	—	—
a	1831	restrike, rev. of 1836	—	—	—	—
b	1831	restrike, rev. of 1852	—	—	—	—
S22	1832	....	154,000	6.50	10.00	45.00
a	1832	rev. side letters recut.............	—	7.00	12.00	49.50
S23	1833	....	120,000	6.00	9.00	39.00
S24	1834	....	141,000	6.00	9.00	39.00
S25	1835	....	398,000	9.00	22.50	55.00
a	1835	recut 5, in date and defective L in liberty	—	11.75	31.00	70.00
b	1835	recut 5, defective L, recut letters on rev.	—	12.50	35.00	85.00
S36	1849	regular issue, large date	39,000	13.00	39.50	90.00
S37	1850	....	39,800	10.50	24.00	60.00
S38	1851	....	147,670	7.00	14.00	45.00
S39	1852	proof only	—	—	—	—
a	1852	restrike	—	—	—	—
S40	1853	....	129,690	7.00	15.00	48.00
a	1853	recut 1	—	9.00	18.00	50.00
S41	1854	....	55,350	7.00	16.00	49.00
S42	1855	....	56,500	7.50	17.00	49.00
S43	1856	....	40,430	7.50	17.00	49.00
S44	1857	....	35,180	12.50	30.00	67.00
a	1857	recut 1	—	13.00	35.00	75.00

	1793	CHAIN TYPE		WREATH TYPE		
Index#	Date	Description	Mintage	Good	Fine	Unc.
S45	1793	wreath type..............................	112,000	150.00	400.00	1500.00
a	1793	wreath, vine & bars....................	—	150.00	400.00	1500.00
b	1793	wreath, strawberry leafs............	—	VERY RARE		
c	1793	wreath, lettered edge one leaf on edge..............................	—	150.00	410.00	—
d	1793	chain type, American..................	—	275.00	700.00	—
e	1793	chain type, period after date........	—	275.00	700.00	—
f	1793	liberty cap type	11,050	350.00	975.00	—
S46	1794	....	918,500	24.00	65.00	—
a	1794	head of 1793	—	45.00	105.00	—
b	1794	head of 1795	—	28.00	67.00	—
c	1794	no fraction bar.........................	—	32.00	90.00	—

1794 STARS UNDER EDGE

d	1794	stars under serrated edge	—	475.00	1600.00	—
S47	1795	....	82,000	17.00	50.00	—
a	1795	Jefferson head, (not regular issue).......	—	150.00	370.00	—
b	1795	lettered edge, one cent high in wr.	—	65.00	150.00	—
c	1795	lettered edge, one cent center in wr........	—	32.00	80.00	—
d	1795	plain edge, one cent high in wr...........	—	32.00	80.00	—
e	1795	plain edge, one cent center in wr.	—	32.00	80.00	—
f	1795	reeded edge,...........................	—	—	—	—
g	1795	double struck, obv.-rev.	—	85.00	250.00	—
S48	1796	liberty cap...............................	974,000	32.00	90.00	—
a	1796	draped bust..............................	—	30.00	80.00	—
b	1796	LIHERTY, die error	—	50.00	165.00	—
c	1796	leaning 6, reverse die br. A-U of United America....................	—	RARE		
S49	1797	....	897,500	14.00	42.00	—
a	1797	stems, rev.	—	16.00	47.00	—
b	1797	stemless, rev............................	—	47.00	140.00	—
c	1797	milled edge, rev. of 1796	—	33.00	85.00	—
d	1797	plain edge, rev. of 1796	—	35.00	85.00	—
e	1797	letter M struck/E in America........	—	42.00	98.00	—
f	1797	double struck, obv.-rev.	—	85.00	175.00	—
S50	1798	....	979,700	9.00	22.00	—
a	1798	98/97.....................................	—	34.00	85.00	—
b	1798	small date...............................	—	14.00	35.00	—
c	1798	large date................................	—	17.00	39.00	—
d	1798	wide date, rev. of 1796	—	27.00	69.00	—
e	1798	close date, rev. of 1796	—	VERY RARE		
S51	1799	rev., chip between E-T of CENT	904,580	240.00	900.00	—

LARGE CENTS

Index #	Date	Description	Mintage	Good	Fine	Unc.
a	1799/98	overdate	—	245.00	925.00	—
b	1799	Rev. shows impression of Lincoln medal	—	—	—	—
S52	1800		2,822,000	8.00	24.00	—
a	1800/1798	overdate	—	10.00	37.00	—
b	1800/179	overdate	—	10.00	36.00	—
S53	1801	blunt 1, normal	1,362,800	9.00	22.00	—
a	1801	first 1 perfect	—	9.00	24.00	—
b	1801	(3) errors, 1/000, one stem, and IINITED	—	25.00	105.00	—
c	1801	rev., 1/000	—	14.00	40.00	—
d	1801	rev., 1/100 over 1/000	—	20.00	85.00	—
S54	1802		3,435,100	7.50	20.00	—
a	1802	single bar, stemless wr.	—	9.00	25.00	—
b	1802	double bar, stemless wr	—	12.00	30.00	—
c	1802	fraction, 1/000	—	13.00	37.00	—
d	1802	rev. double fraction, bar. s/s in states	—	10.00	29.00	—
e	1802	elephant trunk variety die break	—	12.00	35.00	—
S55	1803		2,471,300	7.00	18.00	—
a	1803	small date, sm. fract., blunt 1	—	11.00	24.00	—
b	1803	small date, large fract., blunt 1	—	11.00	24.00	—
c	1803	large date, sm. fract., pointed 1	—	95.00	260.00	—
d	1803	large date, large fract., pointed 1	—	65.00	170.00	—
e	1803	stemless wreath	—	14.00	60.00	—
f	1803	1/100 over 1/000	—	16.00	68.00	—
g	1803	same reverse as (S54d)	—	12.00	37.00	—

1804 RESTRIKE

1804 BROKEN DIE

Index #	Date	Description	Mintage	Good	Fine	Unc.
S56	1804		756,800	140.00	400.00	—
a	1804	broken die, obverse	—	140.00	400.00	—
b	1804	broken die, obv. rev.	—	140.00	400.00	—
c	1804	restrike	—	45.00	85.00	—
S57	1805	blunt 1	941,100	7.00	18.00	—
a	1805	pointed 1	—	9.00	20.00	—
S58	1806		348,000	14.00	50.00	—

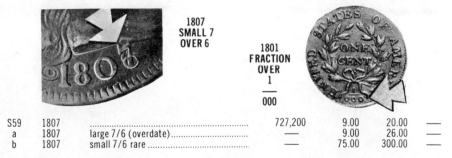

1807
SMALL 7
OVER 6

1801
FRACTION
OVER
1
___
000

Index #	Date	Description	Mintage	Good	Fine	Unc.
S59	1807		727,200	9.00	20.00	—
a	1807	large 7/6 (overdate)	—	9.00	26.00	—
b	1807	small 7/6 rare	—	75.00	300.00	—

LARGE CENTS

Index#	Date	Description	Mintage	Good	Fine	Unc.
c	1807	small fract.	—	8.00	20.00	—
d	1807	large fract.	—	8.00	20.00	—
e	1807	large 7/6, spiked chin	—	9.00	25.00	—
f	1807	comet head, die break	—	14.00	40.00	—
TURBAN HEAD TYPE						
S60	1808	13 stars	1,109,000	11.00	35.00	—
a	1808	12 stars, filled die	—	16.00	50.00	—
S61	1809		222,860	40.00	110.00	—
S62	1810		1,458,500	9.00	30.00	—
a	1810/9	overdate	—	10.00	35.00	—
b	1810	double profile, recut UNITED, rev.	—	55.00	100.00	—
S63	1811		218,000	30.00	70.00	—
a	1811/10	overdate	—	30.00	70.00	—
S64	1812	small date, normal	1,075,500	10.00	27.00	—
a	1812	large date	—	12.00	30.00	—
S65	1813		418,000	12.00	48.00	—
S66	1814	plain 4	357,830	7.00	30.00	—
a	1814	crosslet 4	—	7.00	30.00	—
CORONET TYPE						
S67	1816		2,820,980	5.00	12.00	—

**1817
LARGE CENT
15 STARS**

**1817
LARGE CENT
13 STARS**

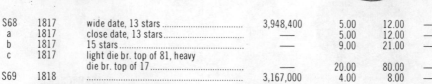

Index#	Date	Description	Mintage	Good	Fine	Unc.
S68	1817	wide date, 13 stars	3,948,400	5.00	12.00	—
a	1817	close date, 13 stars	—	5.00	12.00	—
b	1817	15 stars	—	9.00	21.00	—
c	1817	light die br. top of 81, heavy die br. top of 17	—	20.00	80.00	—
S69	1818		3,167,000	4.00	8.00	—

**1817
WIDE DATE**

1820/19

Index#	Date	Description	Mintage	Good	Fine	Unc.
S70	1819	small date	2,671,000	4.00	8.00	75.00
a	1819	large date	—	4.50	9.00	80.00
b	1819	1819 over 18	—	5.00	11.00	85.00
c	1819/18	triple profile	—	50.00	90.00	200.00
S71	1820	small date	4,407,500	3.50	6.00	50.00
a	1820	large date	—	3.50	6.00	50.00
b	1820/19	overdate	—	8.00	19.00	75.00
S72	1821	wide date	389,000	10.50	36.00	260.00
a	1821	close date	—	13.00	40.00	275.00
S73	1822	wide date	2,072,330	5.00	10.00	95.00
a	1822	close date	—	5.00	10.00	95.00

LARGE CENTS

Index #	Date	Description	Mintage	Good	Fine	Unc.

1833 DOUBLE PROFILE

1823 3 OVER 2

Index #	Date	Description	Mintage	Good	Fine	Unc.
S74	1823	normal, scarce	855,730	26.00	65.00	1400.00
a	1823/22	overdate	—	20.00	60.00	900.00
b	1823	restrike, from broken obv.	—	4.00	10.00	70.00
S75	1824	wide date	1,262,000	5.00	13.00	165.00
a	1824	close date	—	5.00	13.00	165.00
b	1824/22	overdate	—	15.00	30.00	230.00
S76	1825	small A's in legend	1,461,000	4.50	10.00	85.00
a	1825	large A's in legend	—	4.50	10.00	85.00
S77	1826	close date	1,517,425	4.00	9.00	80.00
a	1826	wide date	—	4.00	10.00	85.00
b	1826/25	wide, space, 1826 small dash right of 6.	—	15.00	35.00	275.00
S78	1827		2,357,732	3.00	7.00	65.00
S79	1828	large date	2,260,620	8.00	8.00	65.00
a	1828	small date	—	9.00	17.00	85.00
S80	1829	large letters	1,414,500	3.50	9.00	70.00
a	1829	small letters	—	6.00	17.00	80.00
S81	1830	large letters	1,711,500	3.50	9.00	70.00
a	1830	small letters	—	12.00	40.00	200.00
S82	1831	large letters	3,359,260	3.00	8.00	65.00
a	1831	small letters	—	3.00	8.00	65.00
b	1831	circular die br. through stars	—	9.00	17.00	85.00
S83	1832	large letters	2,362,000	3.00	9.00	65.00
a	1832	small letters	—	3.00	9.00	65.00
b	1832	double profile	—	35.00	95.00	160.00
S84	1833	large letters	—	3.50	7.00	60.00
a	1833	small letters	2,739,000	3.50	7.00	60.00
b	1833	double profile	—	35.00	95.00	160.00
S85	1834	small date, large stars sm. letters on rev.	1,855,100	4.00	11.00	60.00
a	1834	large date, sm. stars, sm. letters on rev.	—	5.00	16.00	75.00
b	1834	large date, large stars, lg. letters on rev.	—	5.00	17.00	90.00

1831 CIRCULAR STAR DIE BREAK

1834 DOUBLE PROFILE

1846 BRAIDED HAIR TYPE

Index #	Date	Description	Mintage	Good	Fine	Unc.
c	1834	double profile	—	35.00	70.00	115.00
S86	1835	lg. date, lg. stars	3,878,000	4.00	10.00	70.00
a	1835	sm. date, sm. stars	—	4.00	10.00	75.00
b	1835	double profile	—	35.00	70.00	125.00
c	1835	double profile, recut Liberty	—	40.00	85.00	140.00
S87	1836		2,111,000	4.00	9.00	60.00

LARGE CENTS

Index #	Date	Description	Mintage	Good	Fine	Unc.
S88	1837	plain cord, sm. let..............................	5,558,300	4.00	9.00	70.00
a	1837	plain cord, lg. let...............................	—	3.00	8.00	45.00
b	1837	beaded hair cord, lg. let.....................	—	3.00	8.00	45.00
S89	1838	....	6,370,200	3.00	8.00	45.00
S90	1839	ty. of 1840, no line	3,128,660	7.00	14.00	85.00
a	1839	booby head, no line under cents..............	—	7.00	12.00	80.00
b	1839	silly hd. line under cents.....................	—	9.00	16.00	90.00
c	1839	ty. of 1838, line under cent	—	6.00	14.00	80.00
d	1839/36	no die br	—	90.00	175.00	—
e	1839/36	die br. center of face to edges line under cents...	—	95.00	195.00	—
S91	1840	large date..	2,462,700	4.00	8.00	55.00
a	1840	small date.......................................	—	4.00	8.00	60.00
S92	1841	....	1,597,300	4.00	8.00	55.00
S93	1842	large date..	2,383,300	3.50	7.00	55.00
a	1842	small date.......................................	—	3.50	7.50	60.00
S94	1843	reverse of 1842..............................	2,428,320	4.00	9.00	65.00
a	1843	obv. of 1842, rev. of 1844	—	18.00	50.00	250.00
b	1843	obv. and rev. of 1844.......................	—	6.00	14.00	80.00
S95	1844	....	2,398,750	3.00	6.00	50.00
a	1844	over 81, rev. die error	—	6.00	15.00	80.00
b	1844	4/4..	—	—	—	—
S96	1845	....	3,894,800	3.00	6.00	30.00

1846 LARGE DATE

1846 SMALL DATE (RECUT)

Index #	Date	Description	Mintage	Good	Fine	Unc.
S97	1846	small date..	4,120,800	3.00	5.00	30.00
a	1846	medium date.....................................	—	3.00	5.50	35.00
b	1846	large date..	—	3.00	7.00	45.00
c	1846	small date, recut date.......................	—	10.00	18.00	60.00
S98	1847	....	6,183,660	2.75	6.50	40.00
a	1847	large date, double 7 & stars.................	—	13.00	40.00	100.00
b	1847	double date.....................................	—	13.00	40.00	115.00
c	1847	large 7 over small 7	—	13.00	45.00	125.00
S99	1848	....	6,415,790	2.75	6.50	40.00
a	1848	struck in hard leather, holed, rare, experimental piece	—	RARE		
S100	1849	....	4,178,000	2.75	6.50	40.00
S101	1850	....	4,426,800	2.75	6.50	40.00
S102	1851	....	9,889,700	2.50	4.50	35.00
a	1851/81	rev. die defect..............................	—	8.00	17.50	100.00
S103	1852	....	5,063,130	2.50	5.50	35.00
a	1852	recut date.......................................	—	3.50	18.00	75.00
S104	1853	....	6,641,131	2.50	6.00	35.00
a	1853	recut date.......................................	—	3.50	19.00	100.00
S105	1854	....	4,236,156	2.00	5.50	35.00
S106	1855	upright 5's..	1,574,829	3.00	7.00	36.00
a	1855	slanted 5's.......................................	—	3.50	8.50	45.00
b	1855	slanted 5's, knob over ear..................	—	4.50	10.00	48.00
S107	1856	upright 5	2,690,463	2.50	6.00	40.00
a	1856	slanting 5...	—	2.50	6.00	40.00

LARGE CENTS

1857 SMALL DATE

1857 LARGE DATE

Index #	Date	Description	Mintage	Good	Fine	Unc.
S108	1857	small date	333,456	18.00	35.00	110.00
a	1857	large date	—	17.00	31.00	105.00

1868 RARE CENT

| S109 | 1868 | probably a trial piece, very rare, proof | — | — | — | — |

Counterstamped large cents and other early U.S. coins are known. These counterstamp coins appear in many various forms, some are genuine while others are man made. Incused counterstamped coins are usually of the name or initial type and man made, yet they can form an interesting and possibly important reference collection.

Other forms of counterstamps appear of various designs and initials, but these are of the raised type from official dies. For example many colonial colonies used the parent country coinage with their own counterstamp to signify the origin due to critical shortage of circulating coins.

FLYING EAGLE CENTS 1856 - 1858

1857 DOUBLE DATE

1856 FLYING EAGLE

The 1856 cent was struck as a pattern coin, only some 1,000 were minted. Due to a shortage of small change the 1856 cent was authorized to be circulated as a regular issue, however, many were hoarded and saved as souvenir pieces, others were circulated.

The 1858 eagle cents have two varieties, one has the large letters and the other small letters. These can be distinguished by the joined A-M of AMERICA which is characteristic of the large letters type.

Index #	Date	Description	Mintage	Good	Fine	Unc.
S110	1856	thin date, open 6, recut 1	1,000	650.00	950.00	2200.00
a	1856	Thick date, close 6	—	650.00	950.00	2200.00
S111	1857		17,450,000	4.50	9.00	100.00
a	1857	double date	—	8.00	16.00	110.00
b	1857	double date and lettering, large blob on wing	—	—	19.00	125.00
S112	1858	small letters	24,600,000	5.50	11.00	130.00
a	1858	large letters	—	6.50	13.00	140.00
b	1858	lg. let. double date	—	9.00	18.00	150.00
c	1858	sm. let. double date	—	9.00	16.00	150.00
d	1858	lg. let. recut ribbon, bow, rev.	—	9.00	18.00	150.00
e	1858	lg. let. 8/7 overdate	—	15.00	50.00	350.00

INDIAN HEAD CENTS (COPPER NICKEL) 1859 - 1864

Index #	Date	Description	Mintage	Good	Fine	Unc.
S113	1859	....	36,400,000	3.50	7.50	90.00
a	1859	recut UNITED STATES	—	4.75	10.00	100.00
b	1859	recut ONE CENT, rev.	—	4.75	10.00	100.00
c	1859	recut 8, date	—	5.50	11.00	100.00
d	1859	filled die date	—	5.50	11.00	100.00
e	1859	recut 1859 over 1859	—	16.00	50.00	175.00
S114	1860	....	20,566,000	3.00	8.00	67.00
a	1860	LIBERTY, die break under 1...................	—	3.50	12.00	75.00
S115	1861	....	10,100,000	8.00	16.00	85.00
a	1861	AMERIC, filled die	—	9.00	20.00	95.00
S116	1862	Reg. Light 2............	28,075,000	2.00	5.00	30.00

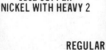

1862 COPPER NICKEL WITH HEAVY 2

REGULAR WITH LIGHT 2

a	1862	heavy 2...	—	3.50	9.00	45.00
b	1862	multiple die breaks...............................	—	3.50	9.00	45.00
S117	1863	....	49,840,000	4.00	8.00	42.00
a	1863	dot after LIBERTY	—	2.00	4.50	27.00
b	1863	part of shield rev. on obv. clash dies........	—	3.00	10.00	35.00
c	1863	recut design rev..................................	—	4.50	13.00	45.00
d	1863	multiple die breaks...............................	—	3.00	9.00	35.00
S118	1864	copper nickel, standard........................	13,740,000	3.00	9.00	35.00
a	1864	recut date	—	4.50	11.50	50.00
b	1864	recut 1..	—	8.00	18.00	70.00
				7.50	16.00	70.00

INDIAN HEAD CENTS (BRONZE)

1864 RECUT DATE

1864 L

It is known that Longacre the designer (L) was entertaining an Indian Chief at his home when his young daughter admiring the Chiefs head bonnet tried it on. This inspired Longacre to submit the present Indian Head cent which was accepted. The Indian Head is actually an inspiration of his daughter.

1864 L POINTED BUST

1864 ROUNDED BUST

S119	1864	(no L on ribbon)...................................	39,233,700	2.50	8.50	65.00
a	1864	(L on ribbon)	—	14.00	45.00	250.00
b	1864	recut date, lettering.............................	—	12.00	26.00	75.00
c	1864	die br. ribbon to C AMERICA	—	3.50	12.00	65.00
d	1864	recut 1...	—	4.50	12.00	70.00

INDIAN CENTS

Index #	Date	Description	Mintage	Good	Fine	Unc.
e	1864	recut 18	—	7.50	16.00	75.00
f	1864	recut 186	—	9.00	22.00	80.00
g	1864	recut date 1864	—	12.00	35.00	85.00
		note the recuts are in various positions				
h	1864L	recut 1	—	18.00	50.00	315.00
i	1864L	recut 18, & America	—	20.00	60.00	320.00
j	1864L	recut 186	—	25.00	70.00	330.00
k	1864L	recut date 1864	—	30.00	80.00	340.00
l	1864L	recut date, lettering	—	35.00	90.00	350.00
m	1864L	triple cut 18	—	30.00	80.00	340.00
S120	1865		35,429,000	2.00	7.00	45.00
a	1865	recut 18	—	6.00	12.00	65.00
b	1865	recut 18, and lettering	—	7.00	15.00	70.00
c	1865	recut lettering	—	6.00	12.00	65.00
d	1865	recut 186	—	8.00	16.00	70.00
e	1865	recut 85	—	7.00	14.00	65.00

**1866
6 OVER 6**

**1867
DOUBLE 1**

Index #	Date	Description	Mintage	Good	Fine	Unc.
S121	1866		9,826,500	9.00	28.00	140.00
a	1866	recut last 6	—	16.00	40.00	175.00
b	1866	recut Liberty, feathers & last 6	—	65.00	100.00	250.00
c	1866	recut 66	—	20.00	60.00	250.00
S122	1867		9,821,000	9.00	27.00	135.00
a	1867	recut 1	—	15.00	40.00	150.00
b	1867	7/small 7	—	25.00	75.00	200.00
c	1867	67/67 overdate—"Halo" in front of profile	—	75.00	150.00	350.00
d	1867	67/67 overdate	—	65.00	135.00	300.00

**1867
67 OVER 67**

69 OVER 9

Note the 1867 overdate is easier to identify than the 1866 and 1869 overdates

Index #	Date	Description	Mintage	Good	Fine	Unc.
S123	1868		10,266,500	9.00	25.00	150.00
a	1868	recut 6 & lettering dble. profile	—	15.00	35.00	200.00
S124	1869		6,420,000	15.00	55.00	300.00
a	1869	9/8 two horns top of 9	—	35.00	85.00	400.00
b	1869	9/9 recut 9	—	25.00	70.00	250.00
c	1869	69/68	—	40.00	90.00	400.00
d	1869	recut AMERICA	—	16.00	35.00	200.00
S125	1870		5,275,000	15.00	42.00	165.00
a	1870	recut U. S. A.	—	16.00	45.00	180.00
S126	1871		3,929,500	20.00	52.00	190.00
a	1871	recut date & U. S. A.—double profile	—	30.00	60.00	200.00
S127	1872		4,042,000	22.00	55.00	260.00
a	1872	recut U. S. A.	—	28.00	60.00	265.00

INDIAN CENTS

Index#	Date	Description	Mintage	Good	Fine	Unc.
S128	1873	....	11,676,500	4.00	15.00	80.00
a	1873	closed 3, recut U.S.A................................	—	5.00	16.00	80.00
b	1873	open 3...	—	5.00	16.00	80.00

1873 REENGRAVED LIBERTY

Index#	Date	Description	Mintage	Good	Fine	Unc.
c	1873	reengraved LIBERTY rare..........................	—	90.00	145.00	425.00
d	1873	recut 73...	—	12.00	29.00	105.00
S129	1874	....	14,187,500	4.00	14.00	80.00
S130	1875	....	13,528,000	4.50	16.00	85.00
a	1875	recut 18 in date	—	14.00	50.00	135.00
S131	1876	....	7,944,000	8.00	18.00	110.00
a	1876	recut U.S. America..................................	—	8.00	24.00	120.00
S132	1877	....	852,500	110.00	220.00	975.00
a	1877	die breaks	—	125.00	190.00	975.00
b	1877	recut UNITED STATES	—	150.00	250.00	1000.00
c	1877	double lips, feather tips...........................	—	150.00	250.00	1000.00
S133	1878	....	5,799,000	7.00	22.00	95.00
S134	1879	....	16,231,000	2.00	6.00	42.00
a	1879	recut U.S. AMERICA................................	—	3.00	10.00	60.00
S135	1880	....	38,964,000	1.00	4.00	27.00
a	1880	recut UNITED STATES	—	2.50	8.00	37.00
S136	1881	....	39,211,000	1.00	4.25	27.00
a	1881	recut U.S. AMERICA................................	—	2.50	8.00	36.00
S137	1882	....	38,581,000	1.25	4.00	27.00
a	1882	recut U.S. AMERICA................................	—	2.50	8.00	36.00
S138	1883	....	45,500,000	1.00	4.00	27.00
a	1883	recut 3 & U.S. AMERICA...........................	—	2.50	7.00	35.00
S139	1884	....	23,261,000	2.50	6.00	38.00
a	1884	recut U.S.A..	—	3.00	8.00	50.00
S140	1885	....	11,765,000	3.75	12.00	60.00
a	1885	recut U.S.A..	—	5.00	15.00	60.00
S141	1886	....	17,654,000	2.00	6.00	45.00
a	1886	last feather points between C-A of AMERICA Type II	—	2.75	9.50	50.00
b	1886	last feather points between I-C of AMERICA Type I recut U.S.A.	—	3.50	12.00	55.00

1906 INDIAN CENT WITH LAST FEATHER POINTED BETWEEN C-A OF AMERICA AS ARE ALL TYPE 2 DATES FROM 1886 TO 1909

BETWEEN I AND C

Index#	Date	Description	Mintage	Good	Fine	Unc.
S142	1887	....	45,226,000	.50	2.00	25.00
a	1887	1-7, filled die	—	3.00	8.00	45.00
S143	1888	....	37,494,000	.50	2.00	25.00
S144	1889	....	48,869,000	.50	2.00	25.00
a	1889	recut one cent rev.	—	1.00	4.50	33.00
S145	1890	....	57,182,000	.50	2.00	23.00
a	1890	recut U.S. AMERICA................................	—	1.00	5.00	33.00

INDIAN CENTS

Index #	Date	Description	Mintage	Good	Fine	Unc.
S146	1891	....	47,072,000	.50	2.50	25.00
a	1891	double date	—	20.00	50.00	90.00
b	1891	recut America	—	1.00	4.00	32.00
S147	1892	....	37,649,800	.75	2.00	25.00
a	1892	double profile	—	2.50	6.50	55.00
S148	1893	....	46,642,000	.50	2.00	25.00
S149	1894	....	16,752,000	1.75	6.00	40.00
a	1894	/94 overdate, rare	—	20.00	45.00	85.00
b	1894	recut one cent rev.	—	2.50	10.50	55.00
c	1894	double date	—	20.00	45.00	85.00
S150	1895	....	38,343,000	.50	2.00	29.00
a	1895	joined loop 9	—	—	—	—
S151	1896	....	39,057,200	.50	2.00	28.00
a	1896	recut 6	—	3.50	11.00	40.00
b	1896	closed 9	—	.75	9.00	35.00
c	1896	closed 9, filled 6	—	2.00	5.50	40.00
S152	1897	....	50,466,000	.50	2.00	25.00

1898 DOUBLE STRUCK

Index #	Date	Description	Mintage	Good	Fine	Unc.
S153	1898	....	49,823,000	.50	2.00	25.00
a	1898	double date	—	16.00	70.00	100.00
b	1898	double die shift, date, profile, lettering....	—	35.00	95.00	250.00
c	1898	double struck	—	—	—	—
S154	1899	....	53,600,000	.40	1.50	22.00
a	1899	double date	—	15.00	65.00	150.00
S155	1900	....	66,833,700	.25	1.25	14.00
S156	1901	....	79,611,000	.25	1.25	12.00
a	1901/1	recut	—	2.75	9.50	35.00
S157	1902	....	87,376,000	.25	1.25	12.00
a	1902	recut (one cent) rev.	—	1.25	2.75	22.00
S158	1903	....	85,094,400	.25	1.25	12.00
a	1903	recut (one cent) rev.	—	1.25	2.75	22.00
S159	1904	....	61,328,000	.25	1.25	12.00
S160	1905	....	80,719,000	.25	1.00	12.00
a	1905	recut, ONE CENT	—	1.25	2.75	22.00
b	1905	double struck	—	45.00	85.00	150.00
S161	1906	....	96,022,000	.25	1.00	12.00
a	1906	recut 6	—	3.50	10.00	35.00
b	1906	recut 19/1906	—	10.00	10.00	35.00
c	1906	recut 1906/90 & recut (one cent) rev.	—	11.50	22.00	55.00
d	1906	close 6	—	—	24.00	60.00
e	1906	open 6	—	—	—	—

INDIAN CENTS

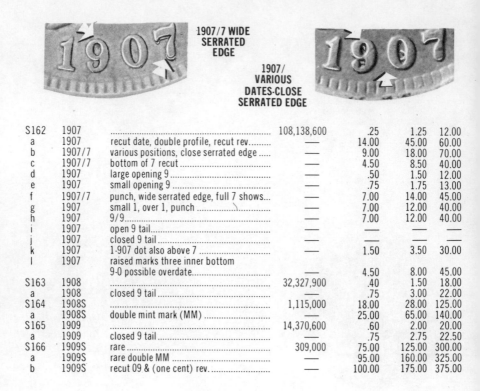

1907/7 WIDE SERRATED EDGE

1907/ VARIOUS DATES-CLOSE SERRATED EDGE

Index #	Date	Description	Mintage	Good	Fine	Unc.
S162	1907	....	108,138,600	.25	1.25	12.00
a	1907	recut date, double profile, recut rev.........	—	14.00	45.00	60.00
b	1907/7	various positions, close serrated edge	—	9.00	18.00	70.00
c	1907/7	bottom of 7 recut	—	4.50	8.50	40.00
d	1907	large opening 9	—	.50	1.50	12.00
e	1907	small opening 9	—	.75	1.75	13.00
f	1907/7	punch, wide serrated edge, full 7 shows...	—	7.00	14.00	45.00
g	1907	small 1, over 1, punch ....\...........	—	7.00	12.00	40.00
h	1907	9/9	—	7.00	12.00	40.00
i	1907	open 9 tail..	—	—	—	—
j	1907	closed 9 tail	—	—	—	—
k	1907	1-907 dot also above 7	—	1.50	3.50	30.00
l	1907	raised marks three inner bottom 9-0 possible overdate............................	—	4.50	8.00	45.00
S163	1908	....	32,327,900	.40	1.50	18.00
a	1908	closed 9 tail	—	.75	3.00	22.00
S164	1908S	....	1,115,000	18.00	28.00	125.00
a	1908S	double mint mark (MM)	—	25.00	65.00	140.00
S165	1909	....	14,370,600	.60	2.00	20.00
a	1909	closed 9 tail	—	.75	2.75	22.50
S166	1909S	rare	309,000	75.00	125.00	300.00
a	1909S	rare double MM	—	95.00	160.00	325.00
b	1909S	recut 09 & (one cent) rev.	—	100.00	175.00	375.00

LINCOLN CENTS

Index #	Date	Description	Mintage	Good	Fine	Unc.

LINCOLN CENTS 1909 - 1966

-IBERTY

(VDB IS THE DESIGNERS INITIALS)   **VICTOR D. BRENNER**

Beware of 1909 S VDB—and other key dates with black coating—they have been noted to have soldered and brazed mint marks—the black coating could be from heating or used to camouflage detection.

Designed by Victor D. Brenner in 1909, his initials appear on the reverse side at bottom rim on some during 1909, others are plain. As of 1918 the initials appear under Lincoln's shoulder, to the present date. 1959 has the Lincoln Memorial Building on the reverse, the design was by Frank Gasparro.

Index #	Date	Description	Mintage	Good	Fine	Unc.
S167	1909	....	72,702,600	.20	.40	7.00
a	1909	micro. shift date	—	1.00	3.50	12.00
S168	1909	VDB	27,995,000	.70	1.00	8.50
a	1909	VDB double struck date	—	15.00	35.00	75.00
b	1909	VDB double date & liberty	—	16.00	40.00	85.00
c	1909	VDB clogged B in Liberty	—	.75	1.50	9.00
S169	1909S	....	1,825,000	25.00	29.00	100.00
a	1909S	double MM	—	37.00	55.00	145.00
S170	1909S	VDB rare	484,000	120.00	150.00	225.00
a	1909S	VDB (IBERTY)	—	140.00	185.00	375.00
S171	1910	....	146,807,000	.10	.50	12.00
S172	1910S	....	6,045,000	3.00	4.00	48.00
a	1910S	double MM, shift south	—	8.00	17.00	75.00

Index #	Date	Description
b	1910S	RHL high MM (Trus-) missing T, Bar......
c	1910S	RHL low MM ....

Index #	Date	Description	Mintage	Good	Fine	Unc.
S172X	1911	....	101,177,000	.10	.50	12.00
a	1911	last 1, slanted	—	1.00	3.00	15.00
S173	1911D	....	12,672,000	1.50	3.50	45.00
a	1911D	last 1, slanted	—	3.50	13.00	52.00
b	1911D	double MM	—	3.75	14.00	55.00
S174	1911S	....	4,026,000	7.50	10.00	76.00
a	1911S	double MM	—	14.00	28.00	100.00

23

LINCOLN CENTS

Index #	Date	Description	Mintage	Good	Fine	Unc.

1911
LAST 1 SLANTED

1918 S
FILLED MINT MARK

Index #	Date	Description	Mintage	Good	Fine	Unc.
S175	1912		68,153,000	.10	.50	18.00
S176	1912D		10,411,000	1.75	4.00	55.00
a	1912D	double MM	—	9.50	16.00	70.00
S177	1912S		4,331,000	4.00	6.00	55.00
a	1912S	double MM	—	10.00	18.00	90.00
S178	1913		76,532,000	.10	.50	15.00
S179	1913D		15,804,000	1.50	6.50	60.00
a	1913D	double MM	—	7.50	14.00	65.00
S180	1913S		6,101,000	3.00	4.50	60.00
a	1913S	double MM	—	9.50	17.00	75.00
b	1913S	LIBERTY, filled die	—	4.00	9.00	70.00
c	1913S	restruck by $2½ gold dies	—	VERY RARE		
S181	1914		75,238,400	.25	.75	35.00
S182	1914D	rare	1,193,000	35.00	55.00	700.00
a	1914D	rare double MM	—	40.00	85.00	725.00
S183	1914S		4,137,000	4.25	6.00	100.00
a	1914S	double MM	—	11.00	26.00	110.00
S184	1915		29,092,000	.40	3.00	70.00
S185	1915D		22,050,000	.60	1.10	30.00
a	1915D	double MM	—	4.50	9.00	65.00
S186	1915S		4,833,000	3.25	4.50	55.00
a	1915S	double MM	—	9.50	17.00	70.00
S187	1916		131,833,000	.10	.50	11.00
S188	1916D		35,956,000	.35	.75	25.00
a	1916D	double MM	—	2.50	7.50	45.00
b	1916D	LIBERTY, filled die	—	2.50	7.50	45.00
S189	1916S		22,510,000	.50	.80	40.00
a	1916S	double MM	—	7.50	14.00	50.00
S190	1917		196,429,000	.10	.40	12.00
a	1917	micro. double date	—	2.75	5.50	18.00
S191	1917D		55,120,000	.30	.60	35.00
a	1917D	double MM	—	3.50	7.00	45.00
S192	1917S		32,620,000	.30	.60	35.00
a	1917S	double MM	—	6.50	13.50	40.00
S193	1918		288,104,600	.10	.40	10.00
S194	1918D		47,830,000	.30	.60	40.00
a	1918D	double MM	—	3.50	8.00	40.00
S195	1918S		34,680,000	.30	.60	40.00
a	1918S	double MM	—	3.50	8.00	45.00
b	1918S	micro. MM, filled	—	.75	3.50	40.00
S196	1919		392,021,000	.10	.50	9.50
S197	1919D		57,154,000	.30	.60	29.00
a	1919D	double MM	—	3.50	7.00	32.00
S198	1919S		139,760,000	.30	.55	22.00
a	1919S	double MM	—	2.75	5.50	33.00
b	1919S	double MM, and 19	—	3.75	12.00	40.00
c	1919S	T-UST, filled die	—	.75	2.75	28.00
d	1919S	skirted R	—	.70	2.50	27.00
e	1919S	filled MM	—	.70	2.50	27.00
S199	1920		310,165,000	.10	.40	10.00
S200	1920D		49,280.000	.25	.75	45.00
a	1920D	broken MM	—	.75	3.00	47.00
b	1920D	double MM	—	3.50	8.50	55.00

LINCOLN CENTS

Index #	Date	Description	Mintage	Good	Fine	Unc.
S201	1920S	....	46,220,000	.25	.50	44.00
a	1920S	double MM............................	—	3.75	8.50	57.00
b	1920S	micro. double date—MM.............	—	6.50	13.50	70.00
S202	1921	....	39,157,000	.10	.60	26.00
a	1921	last 1 slanted........................	—	2.50	5.00	34.00
S203	1921S	....	15,274,000	.60	1.50	200.00
a	1921S	last 1 slanted........................	—	3.50	10.00	170.00
b	1921S	micro. double date...................	—	8.00	17.00	180.00
c	1921S	micro. shift (motto)	—	6.00	11.00	175.00
d	1921S	double MM............................	—	6.00	11.00	175.00
S204	1922D	....	7,160,000	2.75	4.00	45.00
a	1922D	broken MM............................	—	4.00	8.75	55.00
b	1922D	(known as plain) filled die.........	—	30.00	60.00	900.00
c	1922D	horned MM............................	—	3.00	6.75	55.00
d	1922D	micro. double date...................	—	18.00	40.00	130.00
e	1922D	double MM............................	—	6.50	13.50	70.00
S205	1923	....	74,723,000	.10	.50	12.50
a	1923	micro. double date...................	—	1.75	4.50	16.00
S206	1923S	....	8,700,000	.80	2.00	260.00
a	1923S	double MM............................	—	6.50	14.00	280.00
b	1923S	micro, double date & MM............	—	12.00	22.00	300.00
S207	1924	....	75,178,000	.10	.35	20.00
S208	1924D	....	2,520,000	9.00	13.50	200.00
a	1924D	double MM............................	—	18.00	35.00	215.00
b	1924D	various, rotated die, rev............	—	16.00	31.00	205.00
S209	1924S	....	11,696,000	.70	1.75	92.00
a	1924S	double MM............................	—	6.50	13.00	110.00
b	1924S	Goiter................................	—	1.75	5.00	105.00

1925
BROKEN 5

1924
DIEBREAK

Index #	Date	Description	Mintage	Good	Fine	Unc.
S210	1925	....	139,949,000	.10	.35	9.00
a	1925	broken 5..............................	—	1.75	4.00	13.00
b	1925	micro. double date...................	—	1.75	4.00	18.00
c	1925	AMESICA, filled die..................	—	1.75	4.00	15.00
S211	1925D	....	22,580,000	.30	.70	30.00
a	1925D	double MM............................	—	3.50	7.50	45.00
S212	1925S	....	26,380,000	25	.70	40.00
a	1925S	double MM............................	—	4.50	8.50	45.00
S213	1926	....	157,088,000	.10	.30	8.00
a	1926	first 1 slanted.......................	—	1.00	1.75	12.00
S214	1926D	....	28,020,000	20	.50	27.00
a	1926D	double MM............................	—	3.75	8.50	37.00
b	1926D	micro. double date...................	—	4.00	9.50	40.00
S215	1926S	....	4,550,000	2.75	4.75	140.00
a	1926S	double MM............................	—	6.50	12.50	165.00
b	1926S	micro. double date...................	—	8.00	16.00	170.00

1927 D
DOUBLE DATE AND
MINT MARK

LINCOLN CENTS

Index #	Date	Description	Mintage	Good	Fine	Unc.
S216	1927	....	144,440,000	.10	.35	7.50
a	1927	micro double date......................	—	1.50	4.00	20.00
S217	1927 D	....	27,170,000	.25	.50	26.00
a	1927 D	double MM................................	—	3.50	7.50	39.00
b	1927 D	double date & MM	—	4.50	10.00	44.00
S218	1927 S	....	14,276,000	.40	.80	45.00
a	1927 S	double MM................................	—	4.00	9.00	58.00
S219	1928	....	134,116,000	.10	.30	6.50
a	1928	micro. double date.....................	—	2.50	4.50	20.00
S220	1928 D	....	31,170,000	.20	.50	20.00
a	1928 D	double MM................................	—	3.00	7.50	41.00
b	1928 D	micro. double date & MM............	—	4.50	9.00	45.00
S221	1928 S	....	17,266,000	.35	.75	30.00
a	1928 S	double MM................................	—	4.50	8.50	52.00
b	1928 S	micro. double date & MM............	—	5.50	11.50	57.00
c	1928 S	large mint mark	—	.95	2.00	40.00
S222	1929	....	185,262,000	.10	.40	7.00
a	1929	micro. double date.....................	—	2.75	5.50	14.00
S223	1929 D	....	41,730,000	.20	.50	12.50
a	1929 D	double MM, D/L filled die	—	2.00	5.00	18.50
S224	1929 S	....	50,148,000	.20	.50	7.50
a	1929 S	micro. double date & IN GOD WE TRUST..	—	3.75	8.50	17.00
b	1929 S	double MM................................	—	1.25	3.50	12.00
c	1929 S	double date & MM	—	2.75	9.00	20.00
d	1929 S	double date & filled MM	—	3.00	6.00	18.00
e	1929 S	double last 9	—	2.50	8.00	17.00
S225	1930	....	157,415,000	.15	.50	4.75
S226	1930 D	....	40,100,000	.25	.70	10.00
a	1930 D	filled MM	—	.75	2.50	14.00
b	1930 D	filled zero...............................	—	.75	2.50	14.00
c	1930 D	sliced zero...............................	—	.50	1.25	14.50

1928 S LAMINATED

1930 D SLICED ZERO

Index #	Date	Description	Mintage	Good	Fine	Unc.
S227	1930 S	....	24,286,000	.25	.50	9.00
a	1930 S	filled MM	—	.75	2.00	13.50
b	1930 S	double MM................................	—	2.00	8.00	19.00
c	1930 S	sliced zero...............................	—	1.00	2.75	16.00
S228	1931	....	19,396,000	.40	.65	20.00
a	1931	slanted last 1	—	1.00	3.50	22.00
S229	1931 D	....	4,480,000	3.50	4.50	67.00
S230	1931 S	....	866,000	28.00	35.00	60.00
a	1931 S	weak strike, filled die (BERTY) double MM & shifted rev. lettering..................	—	50.00	85.00	130.00
b	1931 S	last 1 slanted	—	30.00	50.00	95.00
S231	1932	....	9,062,000	.70	1.25	16.00
a	1932	slanted 2.................................	—	3.00	5.50	24.00
S232	1932D	....	10,500,000	.60	1.25	16.00
a	1932D	filled MM.................................	—	1.00	2.75	22.00
S233	1933	....	14,360,000	.50	.90	22.00
a	1933	filled 9....................................	—	1.00	3.00	27.00
S234	1933D	....	6,200,000	2.50	3.50	25.00
S235	1934	....	219,080,000	.10	.25	3.50

LINCOLN CENTS

Index #	Date	Description	Mintage	Good	Fine	Unc.
S236	1934D	....	28,446,000	.25	.50	12.00
a	1934D	double MM..................................	—	1.50	4.50	22.00
S237	1935	....	245,388,000	.10	.35	1.50
a	1935	double date & ty in Liberty..............	—	3.50	6.75	14.00
b	1935	Last 5 shift..................................	—	2.00	4.50	10.00
S238	1935D	....	47,000,000	.15	.30	2.50
a	1935D	double date & MM..........................	—	2.75	7.50	14.00
S239	1935S	....	38,702,000	.25	.50	4.00
a	1935S	double MM..................................	—	1.50	4.00	11.00
S240	1936	....	309,637,000	.10	.25	.80
a	1936	micro. double date..........................	—	2.50	5.00	12.50
S241	1936D	....	40,600,000	.15	.35	2.00
a	1936D	micro. double date & MM..................	—	3.00	10.00	16.00
S242	1936S	....	29,130,000	.15	.30	2.75
a	1936 S	double MM..................................	—	3.00	9.00	14.00
b	1936 S	double LIBERTY & MM	—	3.75	12.00	16.00
S243	1937	....	309,179,000	.10	.25	2.25
S244	1937 D	....	50,430,000	.15	.30	1.50
a	1937 D	double MM..................................	—	1.50	3.00	8.50
S245	1937 S	....	34,500,000	.15	.30	2.00
a	1937 S	double MM..................................	—	1.50	2.50	8.50
b	1937 S	double profile..............................	—	.50	1.25	5.00
S246	1938	....	156,696,000	.10	.25	1.50
a	1938	double 9..................................	—	1.50	3.50	5.00
b	1938	double profile..............................	—	1.00	2.00	4.00

**1938 S
LARGE S OVER
SMALL S**

LINCOLN 1939 (1 MISSING)

Index #	Date	Description	Mintage	Good	Fine	Unc.
S247	1938 D	....	20,000,000	.25	.45	3.00
a	1938 D	micro double date..........................	—	1.50	3.25	5.00
S248	1938 S	....	15,180,000	.35	.60	3.50
a	1938 S	double MM large/small S	—	4.75	10.50	19.00
S249	1939	....	316,479,000	.10	.25	.80
a	1939	last 9 shift..................................	—	.70	1.50	5.50
b	1939	micro double date..........................	—	—	—	6.50
S250	1939 D	....	15,160,000	.50	.65	4.75
S251	1939 S	....	52,070,000	.10	.30	1.50
a	1939 S	double MM..................................	—	2.50	6.00	14.00
S252	1940	....	586,825,000	—	.15	.70
a	1940	sliced zero..................................	—	.25	.50	2.00

**1940 S
DOUBLE DATE
MINTMARK**

**1940 D
DOUBLE
MINT MARK**

Index #	Date	Description	Mintage	Good	Fine	Unc.
S253	1940D	....	81,390,000	—	.15	1.50
a	1940D	double MM..................................	—	1.00	3.50	10.00
b	1940D	double date &MM..........................	—	2.00	9.00	12.00
c	1940D	sliced zero..................................	—	.25	.50	2.75
S254	1940S	....	112,940,000	—	.15	1.25
a	1940S	double date & MM..........................	—	2.75	10.00	16.00
b	1940S	double MM..................................	—	1.25	8.00	12.00
c	1940S	double profile..............................	—	.25	1.00	2.50
d	1940S	sliced zero..................................	—	.25	1.00	2.50

LINCOLN CENTS

Index #	Date	Description	Mintage	Good	Fine	Unc.
e	1940S	micro. double LIBERTY	—	.75	1.50	3.50
f	1940S	(BIE) LIBERTY	—	1.00	2.50	5.50
S255	1941		887,039,000	—	.10	1.00
a	1941	last 1 slanted	—	1.00	1.75	4.75
b	1941	first 1 slanted	—	1.00	1.75	4.75
c	1941	filled date 4	—	—	1.00	2.50
d	1941	double (in God We Trust)	—	1.50	3.75	6.50

1941 S LAST 1 SLANTED

1941 D LAST 1 SLANTED

1941 S MICRO DOUBLE DATE DOUBLE

LINCOLN 1941 (1 MISSING)

S256	1941D		128,700,000	.10	.25	1.50
a	1941D	double MM	—	.75	1.75	4.50
b	1941D	BIE (LIBERTY)	—	2.50	12.00	18.00
S257	1941S		92,360,000	.10	.25	1.50
a	1941S	micro. double date & MM	—	2.50	14.00	21.00
b	1941S	double MM	—	1.00	2.00	7.50
c	1941S	microscopic MM	—	.25	.50	2.50
d	1941S	large MM	—	.10	.25	2.00
e	1941S	last 1 slanted	—	1.00	2.00	5.00
S258	1942		657,828,000	—	.10	.45
a	1942	first 1 slanted	—	.50	1.00	3.00
b	1942	BIE LIBERTY, rare	—	—	RARE	—
S259	1942D		206,698,000	—	.15	.55
a	1942D	double MM	—	1.00	2.00	6.75
b	1942D	micro double profile	—	—	—	5.50
c	1942D	various clog liberty	—	—	—	1.75
S260	1942S		85,590,000	.10	.25	4.75
a	1942S	double MM	—	1.00	2.50	10.00
b	1942S	micro. double date & MM	—	2.50	10.00	16.00
c	1942S	large MM	—	.10	.25	6.00
d	1942S	microscopic MM	—	.25	.60	7.00

WAR TIME STEEL CENTS

Due to the shortage of copper during World War II, steel, zinc coated cents were struck during 1943.

1943 S DOUBLE S

DOUBLE DATE AND MINT MARK

The Steel Zinc Coated Cents of 1943

This off-metal issue was first minted in 1943 due to the shortage of the critical war metal copper. Choice Uncirculated cents of 1943 P D S are scarce. The steel cents of 1943 are gradually being retired due to the steel corroding effects.

There are known copper cents of 1943 and steel cents of 1944 both brought about by error during minting production.

LINCOLN CENTS

THE RARE 1943 BRONZE (COPPER) CENTS

Although the U.S. Mint denies any 1943 copper cents were struck, they do exist and are acknowledged by the numismatic field. Three dealers are known to have sold 1943 copper cents and at least six prominent authorities in this field verify that genuine pieces exist.

All 1943 Copper Cents are Rare

1943
BRONZE
CENT
TRIPLE
STRUCK

1943 D OVER 42 D
LINCOLN CENT
DOUBLE
STRUCK

OBVERSE   REVERSE

The above over dates are possibly the result of any ordinary cent finding its way in the press hopper during the striking of the year 1943. Beware of man made pieces manufactured outside of the mint.

Keep in mind the Mint production is similar to factory procedures. Although the utmost care and inspections are made, errors and mistrikes or their likenesses can happen when you consider billions of coins are struck in one year

Index #	Date	Description	Mintage	Good	Fine	Unc.
S261	1943	(steel)	684,628,000	.10	.20	.75
a	1943	micro. double date	—	.25	1.00	3.50
b	1943	micro. double date (43) only	—	.20	.75	2.75
c	1943	Copper, (rare) about 4 known	—		3000.00	
d	1943	Copper, triple struck	—	—	—	—
e	1943	copper, double struck	—	—	—	—
f	1943	copper, struck on 1937 cent, 1943/1937			—	—
g	1943	copper, struck 1943/1942	—	—	—	—
h	1943	copper, struck 1943/1920 S	—	—	—	—
i	1943	Aluminum, struck over Peruvian un centavo	—	—	—	—
j	1943	steel, blob over E (liberty)	—	—	—	2.00
k	1943	various blank digits date	—	—	—	2.50
l	1943	various filled die rev.	—	—	—	1.75
S262	1943 D		217,660,000	.15	.25	1.15
a	1943 D	(copper)	—	—	—	—
b	1943 D	restruck 1943 D/1942 D (copper)	—			
c	1943 D	micro. double date	—	1.00	1.75	5.50
d	1943 D	micro. double date & MM	—	1.50	2.75	7.50
e	1943 D	double MM	—	.50	1.25	5.00
f	1943 D	double 4 & MM	—	1.00	2.00	7.50
g	1943D	various filled die date	—	—	—	2.50
h	1943D	various filled die rev.	—	—	—	2.25
S263	1943 S		191,550,000	.25	.40	1.50
a	1943 S	copper, rare	—		3500.00	
b	1943 S	micro. double date & MM—(RHL)	—	2.00	4.50	12.00
c	1943 S	double MM	—	1.00	2.50	5.50
d	1943 S	clog B, in LIBERTY	—	.25	.75	2.00
e	1943 S	clog MM	—	.25	.75	2.00
f	1943 S	filled die date, various combinations	—	.50	1.25	2.75
g	1943S	various filled die rev.	—	—	—	2.75

LINCOLN CENTS

THE RARE 1943 BRONZE (COPPER) CENTS

The accepted reason for their existence is that some copper blanks of the previous year 1942 found their way to the press during the striking of the 1943 steel cents.

This rare cent is a popular and controversial piece. It is technically a legal tender in all respects. The metal alloy is bronze and the weight and size is the required standard. Legally, when the steel cents were first ordered to be struck, no law was issued that copper would not be struck or considered illegal.

The U.S. Guide Book, mentions the 1943 copper cent and Dr. Judd's U.S. pattern book lists it also.

Care must be taken when buying or selling one of these rare pieces, as there exist possible casts, plated and altered dates.

The 1944 steel cent is a similar case, the only difference being is that the 1943 copper cent is more popular and highly publicized.

The 1943 copper cent is unknown in uncirculated condition. Such a piece if ever found would surely head the list of rarities.

1943 P
BRONZE
CENT

1943/1937

METHODS TO CHECK 1943 COPPER CENTS

1. Check with a magnet for copper plating. A steel copper plated cent will attract to a magnet. Copper, brass, lead, gold, bronze, aluminum and silver will not attract. It's possible to have a coin's molecules disarranged by induction to withstand from being attracted to a magnet.

2. A clear date must be visible. There must be a similar 3 in date as on a 1943 steel cent. There are many coins with dates of 1945 and 1948 that have been mutilated in circulation and resemble a 3. Check date with a high power magnifying glass for any alteration marks. 1948 can easily be altered by cutting away the left side of the 8.

3. Check for the designers initials VDB under Lincoln's shoulder. A cast or copy will not show it.

4. Check the weight, it should be close to 46-48 grains. A cast cent would show tiny pit marks and the features and lettering would be dull.

"Shell Case" Copper Cents 1944-1945

The coloring is different in this issue due to the use of Shell Cases in the mixture of copper alloy during the remelting process. Shortage of copper during the war is the reason for this.

Index#	Date	Description	Mintage	Good	Fine	Unc.
S264	1944	....	1,435,400,000	—	.10	.45
a	1944	slanted 1...	—	.50	.75	1.25
b	1944	last 4 double..	—	.50	1.00	2.50
c	1944	(BIE) LIBERTY	—	1.50	4.50	16.00
d	1944	die break, last 4 (Cross of Lorraine)	—	1.50	4.50	13.50
e	1944	broken 1 & 9 (filled die)..........................	—	—	2.50	6.50
f	1944	die break, extra 1, 19441	—	—	3.50	10.00
g	1944	filled die,———ERTY............................	—	1.00	2.50	6.00
h	1944	dots. (LIB:ERTY)......................................	—	—	3.00	7.00
i	1944	(steel) (3) known.....................................	—	—	600.00	1200.00
j	1944	Steel die break under W (we), top left O of one to L of Plubibus, also from lapel over shoulder to bottom rim.....................	—	—	—	—

LINCOLN CENTS

Index #	Date	Description	Mintage	Good	Fine	Unc.

1944 D STEEL

1944 D COPPER

Index #	Date	Description	Mintage	Good	Fine	Unc.
S265	1944D		430,578,000	—	.15	.45
a	1944D	micro double 4's	—	—	2.50	3.00
b	1944D	open top last 4	—	—	1.50	2.50
c	1944D	double MM, North	—	1.00	3.00	8.00
d	1944D	double date & MM	—	2.00	4.50	9.00
e	1944D	(BIE) LIBERTY	—	3.00	10.00	35.00
f	1944D	steel	—	—	1500.00	—
S266	1944S		282,760,000	—	.10	.50
a	1944S	double MM	—	1.00	3.50	9.00
b	1944S	micro. double date	—	1.00	3.50	9.00
c	1944S	micro. double date & MM	—	1.50	4.50	10.00
d	1944S	micro. double profile	—	.50	2.00	4.50
e	1944S	ghost image of Lincoln on rev	—	.10	.25	1.00
S267	1945		1,040,515,000	—	—	.50
a	1945	micro. double date	—	.50	2.00	5.00
b	1945	(BIE) LIBERTY	—	3.00	9.00	20.00
c	1945	filled die (LI ERTY)	—	.75	2.00	4.00
d	1945	various filled die liberty	—	—	—	1.75
e	1945	various clog liberty	—	—	—	1.75
f	1945	laminated peeled type	—	—	2.00	—
S268	1945D		226,268,000	—	.10	.55
a	1945D	Double MM	—	1.00	3.50	7.00
b	1945D	double 4	—	1.00	4.00	7.50
c	1945D	clog B, LIBERTY	—	.20	.50	1.75

**1944
BROKEN
1 AND 9**

**1945 S
SLASH MARK
(DIE BREAK)**

Index #	Date	Description	Mintage	Good	Fine	Unc.
S269	1945S		181,770,000	—	.10	.60
a	1945S	double MM	—	1.00	4.00	8.00
b	1945S	slash mark (God/We)	—	1.00	2.00	4.50
c	1945S	comma, (19,45 S)	—	1.00	2.00	4.50
d	1945S	slanted I in (LIBERTY)	—	.25	1.00	2.25
e	1945S	broken MM	—	.25	.50	1.50
S270	1946		991,655,000	—	—	.40
a	1946	(R.T.) dot in Liberty	—	—	.65	4.50
S271	1946D		315,690,000	—	—	.50
a	1946D	double MM	—	1.00	2.75	4.00
b	1946D	slanted I	198,100,000	—	—	1.00
S272	1946S		—	—	.20	.65
a	1946S	double MM	—	.75	1.50	3.75
S273	1947		190,555,000	—	—	.75
a	1947	double lettering (STATE OF AMERICA)	—	.75	1.50	3.50
b	1947	shifted 7	—	1.00	4.00	5.00
S274	1947D		194,750,000	—	—	.55
a	1947D	double MM	—	1.00	4.00	6.00
b	1947D	double MM & shifted 7	—	2.00	5.00	9.00

LINCOLN CENTS

Index #	Date	Description	Mintage	Good	Fine	Unc.
c	1947D	various filled die (liberty)	—	—	.75	1.75
d	1947D	various blobs in (liberty)	—	—	.75	1.75
S275	1947S		99,000,000	—	.15	.90
a	1947S	double MM	—	1.00	2.75	6.00
b	1947S	long curved 7	—	—	—	3.50

LONG CURVED 7

Index #	Date	Description	Mintage	Good	Fine	Unc.
S276	1948		317,570,000	—	—	.65
a	1948	double 4	—	1.00	2.50	6.00
b	1948	(BIE) LIBERTY	—	2.00	5.00	10.00
S277	1948D		172,637,000	—	—	.65
a	1948D	double MM	—	1.00	2.50	6.00
b	1948D	(BIE) LIBERTY	—	1.00	4.50	9.00
S278	1948S		81,735,000	—	—	1.25
S279	1949		217,490,000	—	—	.75
a	1949	slanted 1	—	.75	1.50	4.50
b	1949	sliced 9	—	.50	1.00	2.75
S280	1949D		154,370,000	—	—	.75
a	1949D	double MM Shift South	—	1.00	2.50	6.00
b	1949D	clog MM	—	—	.50	1.75
c	1949D	clog 4	—	—	.50	1.75

1949 S DOUBLE MINT MARK

LINCOLN 1952 (2 MISSING)

Index #	Date	Description	Mintage	Good	Fine	Unc.
S281	1949S		64,290,000	—	—	2.50
a	1949S	double MM	—	1.00	3.50	8.00
S282	1950		272,686,000	—	—	.75
a	1950	(BIE) LIBERTY	—	.50	1.50	3.50
b	1950	sliced zero	—	—	.50	2.50
S283	1950D		334.950,000	—	—	.75
a	1950D	micro. double date	—	1.00	2.50	5.50
b	1950D	double MM Close over lap shift east	—	1.00	2.50	5.50
c	1950D	(BIE) LIBERTY	—	.50	1.50	3.00
d	1950D	connected 9-5	—	.25	.50	1.25
e	1950D	connected 9MM	—	.25	.50	1.25

1950 ?/9

1951 D CLOGGED MINT MARK

Index #	Date	Description	Mintage	Good	Fine	Unc.
f	1950D	clog upper 5	—	.25	.50	.75
g	1950D	1?50 DIE BR. TIP OF 9	—	.50	.75	5.00
h	1950D	sliced zero	—	.25	.50	2.00
i	1950D	Blob 9-5 MM	—	.25	.50	1.75

32

LINCOLN CENTS

Index #	Date	Description	Mintage	Good	Fine	Unc.
S284	1950S	....	118,505,000	—	—	.95
a	1950S	double MM	—	1.00	1.75	4.50
b	1950S	(BIE) LIBERTY	—	1.00	2.00	4.50
c	1950S	sliced zero	—	.25	.75	3.50
S285	1951	....	294,633,000	—	—	.75
a	1951	last 1 slanted	—	.15	1.00	2.50
b	1951	(BIE) LIBERTY	—	1.00	3.50	7.00
c	1951	brockage, double obv., on obv.-rev.	—	—	9.00	—
S286	1951D	....	625,355,000	—	—	.35
a	1951D	double overlap shift N. E.	—	1.00	1.75	5.50
b	1951D	slanted last I	—	.40	1.50	3.00
c	1951D	LIBERTY, clogged I	—	.25	1.00	2.00
d	1951D	(BIE) LIBERTY	—	.50	1.00	4.00
e	1951D	clog 9	—	.10	.25	.75
f	1951D	Micro. double date & MM	—	1.00	2.00	4.50
g	1951D	clog R upper & skirted lower R	—	.25	.35	.75
h	1951D	LIBERTY, filled die	—	.10	.35	.75
i	1951D	(BIE)joined 9-D-5, Double MM, Shift N. E.	—	1.00	3.00	6.00
S287	1951S	....	100,890,000	.10	.20	1.50
a	1951S	double MM	—	1.00	1.75	5.75
b	1951S	last 1 slanted	—	.10	1.00	4.00
c	1951S	various clog parts of numbers	—	.25	.40	1.00
d	1951S	(BIE) LIBERTY	—	1.00	2.00	5.50
e	1951S	Blob under "E", blob between 9-5-MM	—	1.00	3.00	6.50
f	1951S	various clog letters in LIBERTY	—	.25	.40	1.00
S288	1952	....	186,856,000	—	—	.85

1952 LINCOLN HORNED HEAD

1952 D S D

a	1952	horned head	—	1.00	3.00	12.00
b	1952	horned (W/E) head	—	1.00	3.00	12.00
c	1952	(BIF) LIBERTY	—	1.00	3.00	10.00
d	1952	various clog parts of LIBERTY	—	.25	.40	.75
e	1952	clog lower $^1_2$ of 5	—	.25	.40	.75
S289	1952D	....	746,130,000	—	—	.35
a	1952D	double MM	—	1.00	1.50	4.50
b	1952D	double date & MM	—	1.50	2.00	5.50
c	1952D	(BIE) LIBERTY	—	—	3.00	—
d	1952D	connected 9-5	—	.25	.40	1.00
e	1952D	various clog numbers	—	.25	.40	1.00
f	1952D	various clog parts of LIBERTY	—	.25	.40	1.00
g	1952D	connected 9 & MM	—	.25	.50	1.25
h	1952D	flying D (Die breaks)	—	.25	.50	1.50
i	1952D	filled die 19	—	.25	.50	1.50
j	1952D	Horn double MM overlapping	—	—	—	5.50

LAMINATED TYPE

CLOGGED 5

LINCOLN CENTS

Index #	Date	Description	Mintage	Good	Fine	Unc.
S290	1952S	....	137,800,000	—	—	1.25
a	1952S	(BIE) LIBERTY..................................	—	1.00	3.00	12.00
b	1952S	connected 5-MM	—	.25	.50	1.00
c	1952S	clog MM	—	.15	.25	1.00
d	1952S	various clog parts of LIBERTY	—	.15	.40	1.00
e	1952S	various clog numbers........................	—	.15	.40	1.00
f	1952S	clog 5, dot/shoulder, dot between "E" & stalk, rev...............................	—	.75	3.50	7.50
g	1952S	peeling laminated type	—		2.00	—

1953 P SHIFT 3

1953 P REGULAR

Index #	Date	Description	Mintage	Good	Fine	Unc.
S291	1953	....	256,883,000	—	—	.50
a	1953	micro. double date............................	—	1.00	3.00	8.00
b	1953	(BIE) LIBERTY..................................	—	1.00	2.75	7.00
c	1953	(RJ) connected R-T in LIBERTY	—	1.00	2.75	7.50
d	1953	shifted 3	—	1.00	2.75	5.50
e	1953	shifted 3, recut I in LIBERTY	—	1.25	3.00	6.00
f	1953	shifted 3, recut I in LIBERTY with die break I to God	—	1.50	3.50	6.50

1953 LIBIERTY

1953 P R J DIE BREAK

Index #	Date	Description	Mintage	Good	Fine	Unc.
g	1953	3/3 shift north, dot over R long I in liberty	—	—	—	
h	1953	various blobs in liberty	—	—	—	.75
i	1953	clog 9..	—	—	—	—
S292	1953D	....	700,515,000	—	—	.50
a	1953D	double MM perfect parallel	—	.75	1.50	19.00
b	1953D	(BIE) LIBERTY..................................	—	.50	1.00	9.50
c	1953D	various clog parts of LIBERTY	—	.10	.35	1.00
d	1953D	various clog numbers........................	—	.10	.35	1.00
e	1953D	double MM D/broken D, East shift	—	.50	1.50	10.00
f	1953D	UBE(LIBERTY)...................................	—	—	—	.50
g	1953D	close overlapping shift N. E.	—	—	—	5.00

1953 S CLOGGED 9 AND 5

1953 HIGH S TOUCHING 5

Index #	Date	Description	Mintage	Good	Fine	Unc.
S293	1953S	....	181,835,000	—	.20	.80
a	1953S	(BIE) LIBERTY..................................	—	.50	2.50	10.00
b	1953S	double MM, Die break left "We"	—	1.00	3.00	10.00
c	1953S	clogged 9-MM	—	.25	.75	1.00
d	1953S	various clog numbers........................	—	.10	.35	1.00
e	1953S	various clog parts of LIBERTY	—	.20	.50	1.00
f	1953S	MM touching 5..................................	—	.20	.60	1.00
g	1953S	last 3 shift	—	1.50	2.00	7.50

34

Index #	Date	Description	Mintage	Good	Fine	Unc.

CLOGGED 9

CLOGGED 9

Index #	Date	Description	Mintage	Good	Fine	Unc.
S294	1954	....	71,873,000	.10	.20	1.00
a	1954	(BIE) LIBERTY	—	1.00	2.50	12.00
b	1954	LBBERTY, die break	—	1.00	3.00	12.00
c	1954	shifted 4	—	1.00	2.75	6.00
d	1954	double legend & motto	—	1.00	2.75	6.00
S295	1954D	....	251,552,000	—	—	.50
a	1954D	(BIE) LIBERTY	—	.50	1.50	4.00
b	1954D	double MM..	—	.50	2.50	9.00
c	1954D	micro. double date & MM	—	.75	3.00	10.00
d	1954D	various clog parts of LIBERTY	—	.10	.50	1.00
e	1954D	various clog numbers........................	—	.10	.50	1.00

1954 D
DOUBLE
MINT MARK

1954 S
JOINED
S AND 9

Index #	Date	Description	Mintage	Good	Fine	Unc.
S296	1954S	....	96,100,000	—	—	.75
a	1954S	(BIE) LIBERTY	—	.25	.75	3.50
b	1954S	dot in front of date, clog 9	—	.25	1.00	4.00
c	1954S	(SJ) MM die break J shape, 5 to S	—	.75	2.50	9.00
d	1954S	clog 9, joined MM-5, plug low B	—	.50	1.50	2.75
e	1954S	connected 9-MM...........................	—	.25	1.00	1.75
f	1954S	various clog parts of LIBERTY	—	.10	.35	.75
g	1954S	various clog numbers...........................	—	.10	.35	.75
h	1954S	Blob between R-T of Liberty...................	—	.10	.35	.75
i	1954S	double MM..	—	.50	1.50	3.50

1955 DOUBLE
DIE SHIFT

1955 LAST 5
SHIFT

Index #	Date	Description	Mintage	Good	Fine	Unc.
S297	1955	....	330,958,000	—	—	.35
a	1955	double die shift, our est.	35,000	60.00	150.00	400.00
b	1955	micro. shift date...........................	—	.50	3.50	10.00
c	1955	last 5 shift..	—	.25	.50	3.00
d	1955	last 5 shift, dot E in LIBERTY	—	.50	1.00	4.50
e	1955	(BIE) LIBERTY	—	.50	1.50	4.50
f	1955	various clog parts of LIBERTY	—	.25	1.00	5.50
g	1955	various clog numbers...........................	—	.10	.30	.75
h	1955	thick planchet..	—	.20	1.00	4.50
i	1955	(UB) Liberty, joined LI	—	.50	1.50	5.50
j	1955	micro. double shift date & Liberty (Proof)..	—	—	—	350.00

LINCOLN CENTS

Index #	Date	Description	Mintage	Good	Fine	Unc.
S298	1955D	....	563,257,000	—	—	.40
a	1955D	double MM close overlap......................	—	.50	1.50	8.00
b	1955D	(BIE) LIBERTY	—	.50	1.50	4.50
c	1955D	(IIB) LIBERTY	—	.75	3.00	8.50
d	1955D	various clog parts of LIBERTY	—	.25	.50	1.25
e	1955D	various clog numbers...........................	—	.25	.50	1.00
f	1955D	(IIB) & (BiE) incomplete, (LIBERTY) clog-filled die.......................	—	3.00	7.00	16.00
g	1955D	clog T in CENT	—	.10	.50	.75
h	1955D	(RHL)..	—	—	.15	.50
i	1955D	(PHL)..	—	—	—	.25
j	1955D	joined 9-5..	—	—	—	1.25
k	1955D	micro double date...............................	—	—	—	3.50
l	1955D	double MM D/L	—	—	—	5.00

1955 S SLASHED S

1955S TWINS OFF CENTER

Index #	Date	Description	Mintage	Good	Fine	Unc.
S299	1955S	....	44,610,000	.25	.35	.75
a	1955S	double MM..	—	.50	1.50	15.00
b	1955S	(BIE) LIBERTY	—	.25	.50	1.25
c	1955S	(BiE) incomplete	—	.25	.50	1.25
d	1955S	connected bottom of (BE) LIBERTY	—	.25	.35	1.00
e	1955S	various clog parts of LIBERTY	—	.25	.35	1.00
f	1955S	various clog numbers...........................	—	.25	.50	1.00
g	1955S	slashed MM, S/	—	.35	1.00	3.00
h	1955S	(IIB) LIBERTY	—	.50	1.25	4.50
i	1955S	Horned "B" bracket BE LIBERTY............	—	.75	1.50	4.50
j	1955S	Die break through "Plurbus" rev..............	—	.35	.75	2.50
k	1955S	Tates (states) MM, dagger S	—	—	—	2.00
l	1955S	various clog date	—	—	—	1.75
m	1955S	RHL..	—	—	—	1.50
S300	1956	....	421,414,000	—	—	.25
a	1956	(BIE) LIBERTY & crack Skull	—	.50	1.00	2.75
b	1956	(IIBIE) LIBERTY, (LIIBIERTY)	—	.75	2.00	12.00
c	1956	various clog parts of LIBERTY	—	.15	.35	.75
d	1956	various clog numbers...........................	—	.15	.35	.75
e	1956	(EIR) LIBERTY, with crack skull	—	.50	1.00	2.50

**1956
DOUBLE MINT MARK
(BIE) IN LIBERTY**

**1957 D
DOUBLE D
SHIFTED**

Index #	Date	Description	Mintage	Good	Fine	Unc.
S301	1956D	....	1,098,200,000	—	—	.20
a	1956D	(BIE) LIBERTY	—	.25	.50	1.50
b	1956D	various clog parts of LIBERTY	—	.20	.35	.75
c	1956D	various clog numbers...........................	—	.20	.35	.75

LINCOLN CENTS

Index #	Date	Description	Mintage	Good	Fine	Unc.
d	1956D	double MM (perfect parallel)	—	.50	1.50	15.00
e	1956D	perf. paral. double MM & (BIE)	—	1.00	4.00	24.00
f	1956D	double profile, LIBERTY-date	—	1.00	3.50	20.00
g	1956D	pointed curl 9 (in loop)	—	—	.25	.50
h	1956D	double MM, light D South	—	—	.50	4.50
i	1956D	sliced 6	—	—	.25	1.00
j	1956D	double MM, D/broken D, south shift	—	—	1.25	8.50
k	1956D	(UBE) LIBERTY	—	.25	.75	2.75
S302	1957		283,787,000	—	—	.20
a	1957	(BIE) LIBERTY	—	.25	.75	1.00
b	1957	slanted 1	—	.25	.50	1.00
c	1957	various clog parts of LIBERTY	—	.10	.25	.50
d	1957	various clog numbers	—	.10	.25	.50
e	1957	(BIE) with r957 (die break)	—	.50	1.25	2.75

1957 D DOUBLE DATE CLOGGED LOWER B

1957 D MICRO DOUBLE DATE

S303	1957D		1,051,342,000	—	—	.20
a	1957D	(BIE) LIBERTY	—	.25	.50	1.00
b	1957D	(BIE) incomplete 1, to crack skull	—	.25	.50	1.00
c	1957D	double MM (perfect parallel)	—	.50	2.00	9.00
d	1957D	(RHL) rounded hairline, also called loose tupee	—	—	—	.50
e	1957D	micro. double date—clog 9	—	1.00	2.50	4.50
f	1957D	micro. double date—MM	—	1.50	3.50	7.00
g	1957D	double profile	—	—	.50	.75
h	1957D	slanted 1	—	.25	1.00	2.50
i	1957D	goatee chin—joined 9 & MM, clog 5	—	.50	2.00	3.00
j	1957D	close overlapping MM	—	—	.50	1.00
k	1957D	micro. double date, clog lower B & 9	—	.50	1.00	5.00
l	1957D	double MM, shifted South	—	—	.75	3.50
m	1957D	various clog parts of LIBERTY	—	.20	.40	.75
n	1957D	various clog numbers	—	.20	.40	.75
o	1957D	(BIE) and double MM	—	.50	2.00	4.50
p	1957D	neck-less, filled die	—	—	.50	2.00
q	1957D	(UBE) LIBERTY	—	.50	1.00	3.00
r	1957D	triple MM close overlapping	—	—	—	7.00
s	1957D	double MM shift N. E.	—	—	—	3.75
t	1957D	double shift stalks on rev	—	—	—	6.50
u	1957D	1957-D & tail 9	—	—	—	3.50

1957 D CLOGGED 9 AND 5

1957 D ROLLED FOLD

S304	1958		253,400,000	—	—	.30
a	1958	(BIE) LIBERTY	—	.50	1.00	8.50
b	1958	(BEI) LIBERTY	—	.50	1.00	9.50
c	1958	various clog parts of LIBERTY	—	.10	.40	.75

LINCOLN CENTS

Index #	Date	Description	Mintage	Good	Fine	Unc.

**1958 D
DIE BREAK UNDER D
D LOOKS LIKE P**

Index #	Date	Description	Mintage	Good	Fine	Unc.
d	1958	various clog numbers.........................	—	.10	.40	.75
e	1958	chin to bowtie (clash dies)......................	—	.10	.40	.75
f	1958	thin date.......................................	—	—	.10	.35
g	1958	Thick Date.....................................	—	—	.10	.25
h	1958	micro. double date............................	—	.50	1.00	4.00
i	1958	double die shift...............................	—	—	—	150.00
S305	1958D	....	800,953.000	—	—	.10

**1958 D
DOUBLE
MINT MARK**

**1958 D 5 AND D
CONNECTED**

Index #	Date	Description	Mintage	Good	Fine	Unc.
a	1958D	Double MM	—	.50	.75	2.00
b	1958D	micro. double date & MM	—	.75	1.50	4.00
c	1958D	MM looks like "P" (die Br.).....................	—	.25	.50	1.50
d	1958D	connected MM & 5	—	.25	.50	1.00
e	1958D	(BIE) LIBERTY	—	.50	1.50	4.50
f	1958D	r958, referred to as rev. 1.....................	—	.25	.50	1.50
g	1958D	r958 & micro. double date......................	—	.50	1.00	3.50
h	1958D	various clog parts of LIBERTY	—	.10	.25	.75
i	1958D	various clog numbers..........................	—	.10	.25	.75
j	1958D	partial micro. double date	—	.25	.75	1.25
k	1958D	(Die break under (D) MM	—	.25	.50	1.00
l	1958D	Die Break/S (Trust)	—	—	.25	1.00
m	1958D	triple MM shift N.	—	—	—	8.50
S306	1959	....	610,864,291	—	—	.20
a	1959	slanted 1......................................	—	.25	.75	1.50
b	1959	(BIE) LIBERTY	—	.25	.75	2.00
c	1959	thin date......................................	—	—	.10	.35
d	1959	thick date.....................................	—	—	—	.25
e	1959	(RHL) rounded hairline	—	—	—	.35
f	1959	(PHL) pointed hairline.........................	—	—	—	.20
g	1959	various clog parts of LIBERTY	—	—	.25	.50
h	1959	various clog numbers..........................	—	—	.25	.50
i	1959	various clog letters, rev. side..................	—	—	.25	.50

**1959 D
TRIPLE MINT MARK**

**1958D
LINE OVER S
IN TRUST**

Index #	Date	Description	Mintage	Good	Fine	Unc.
S307	1959D	1,279,760,000		—	—	.10
a	1959D	double MM perfect parallel	—	1.00	1.50	3.50
b	1959D	triple MM, D/D over partial D	—	1.00	2.50	5.50
c	1959D	micro. double date.............................	—	.50	1.25	3.50
d	1959D	double bar 5...................................	—	.10	.50	1.00
e	1959D	double MM, D/partial D, clog 9.................	—	.50	.75	3.50
f	1959D	double MM, close overlapping D's............	—	.25	.50	1.50
g	1959D	double profile	—	.25	.50	1.25
h	1959D	recut LIBERTY.................................	—	.50	1.50	2.00
i	1959D	thin date	—	—	—	.20
j	1959D	thick date.....................................	—	—	—	.15

LINCOLN CENTS

Index#	Date	Description	Mintage	Good	Fine	Unc.
k	1959D	(RHL) rounded hairline	—	—	—	.30
l	1959D	(PHL) pointed hairline	—	—	—	.15
m	1959D	(BIE) LIBERTY	—	.25	1.00	3.00
n	1959D	various clog parts of Liberty	—	.10	.40	.75
o	1959D	various clog numbers	—	.10	.40	.75
p	1959D	double date & MM	—	.50	2.00	5.75
q	1959D	connected 9-MM	—	.20	.40	.75
r	1959D	cross in date, die break thru 1 (clash dies)	—	—	—	.50
s	1959D	double MM shift N. E.	—	—	—	3.75
S308	1960	all kinds	588,096,000	—	—	.10
a	1960	small date, our estimate less than	700,000	2.50	4.25	6.50
b	1960	medium date (thin) our est.	60,000,000	—	—	.30
c	1960	large date	—	—	—	.10
d	1960	small date (proof) our est. (in set)	35,000	PROOF $42.00		
e	1960	(RHL) small date	—	1.00	3.00	8.00
f	1960	(PHL) small date	—	1.00	2.50	7.50
g	1960	small date, thin	—	1.00	2.50	7.50
h	1960	small date, thick	—	1.00	2.50	7.50
i	1960	small date (proof) large date reengraved over small date & LIBERTY (in set)		PROOF SET $125.00		
j	1960	comma, 19,60	—	—	.40	1.00
k	1960	connected 9-6	—	—	.40	1.00
l	1960	various clog parts of LIBERTY (sm. date)	—	—	.50	2.50
m	1960	various clog numbers (sm. date)	—	—	.50	2.50
n	1960	various clog parts of LIBERTY (lg. date)	—	—	.25	1.00
o	1960	various clog numbers (lg. date)	—	—	.25	1.00
p	1960	19610 (damaged zero)	—	—	.25	1.00

1960 SMALL DATE

1960 LARGE DATE

How To Recognize The Small-Medium-Large Date Cents Of 1960 P-D

SMALL DATE The top of 19 even, tail end of 6 is short, zero inner diameter is small. Any date prior to 1960 is considered as small dates.

MEDIUM Same as the large date, only difference being the numbers are quite thin in comparison to the large date. Many of the thin medium dates have been confused as small dates.

LARGE The top of 9 is slightly higher than the 1, the tail of 6 is longer, the zero diameter is larger.

Compare by having a large and small date cent together, issues from P and D mints are the same.
Beware of small dates with the MM removed, tiny tool marks can be seen.

	1960 D LIGHT D NORTH		
LARGE DATE		SMALL DATE	

S309	1960D	all kinds	1,580,884,000	—	—	.10
a	1960D	small date our est. less than	70,000,000	—	.15	.40
b	1960D	medium date our est.	60,000,000	—	.15	.30
c	1960D	large date	—	—	—	.10
d	1960D	sm., double MM, light D North	—	—	1.00	6.00

LINCOLN CENTS

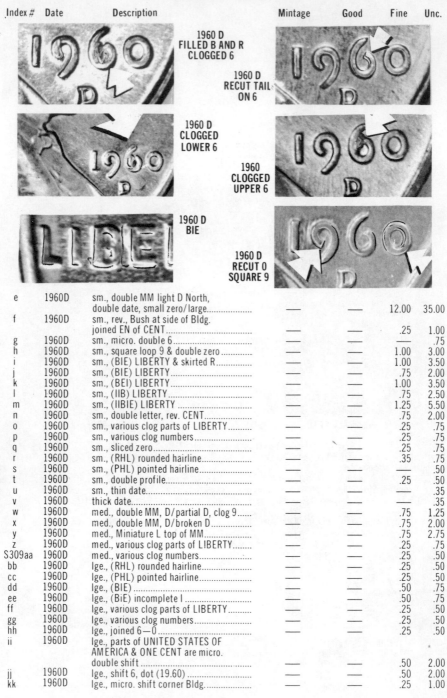

Index #	Date	Description	Mintage	Good	Fine	Unc.
		1960 D FILLED B AND R CLOGGED 6				
		1960 D RECUT TAIL ON 6				
		1960 D CLOGGED LOWER 6				
		1960 CLOGGED UPPER 6				
		1960 D BIE				
		1960 D RECUT 0 SQUARE 9				
e	1960D	sm., double MM light D North, double date, small zero/large	—	—	12.00	35.00
f	1960D	sm., rev., Bush at side of Bldg. joined EN of CENT	—	—	.25	1.00
g	1960D	sm., micro. double 6	—	—	—	.75
h	1960D	sm., square loop 9 & double zero	—	—	1.00	3.00
i	1960D	sm., (BIE) LIBERTY & skirted R	—	—	1.00	3.50
j	1960D	sm., (BIE) LIBERTY	—	—	.75	2.00
k	1960D	sm., (BEI) LIBERTY	—	—	1.00	3.50
l	1960D	sm., (IIB) LIBERTY	—	—	.75	2.50
m	1960D	sm., (IIBIE) LIBERTY	—	—	1.25	5.50
n	1960D	sm., double letter, rev. CENT	—	—	.75	2.00
o	1960D	sm., various clog parts of LIBERTY	—	—	.25	.75
p	1960D	sm., various clog numbers	—	—	.25	.75
q	1960D	sm., sliced zero	—	—	.25	.75
r	1960D	sm., (RHL) rounded hairline	—	—	.35	.75
s	1960D	sm., (PHL) pointed hairline	—	—	—	.50
t	1960D	sm., double profile	—	—	.25	.50
u	1960D	sm., thin date	—	—	—	.35
v	1960D	thick date	—	—	—	.35
w	1960D	med., double MM, D/partial D, clog 9	—	—	.75	1.25
x	1960D	med., double MM, D/broken D	—	—	.75	2.00
y	1960D	med., Miniature L top of MM	—	—	.75	2.75
z	1960D	med., various clog parts of LIBERTY	—	—	.25	.75
S309aa	1960D	med., various clog numbers	—	—	.25	.50
bb	1960D	lge., (RHL) rounded hairline	—	—	.25	.50
cc	1960D	lge., (PHL) pointed hairline	—	—	.25	.50
dd	1960D	lge., (BIE)	—	—	.50	.75
ee	1960D	lge., (BiE) incomplete I	—	—	.50	.75
ff	1960D	lge., various clog parts of LIBERTY	—	—	.25	.50
gg	1960D	lge., various clog numbers	—	—	.25	.50
hh	1960D	lge., joined 6—0	—	—	.25	.50
ii	1960D	lge., parts of UNITED STATES OF AMERICA & ONE CENT are micro. double shift	—	—	.50	2.00
jj	1960D	lge., shift 6, dot (19.60)	—	—	.50	2.00
kk	1960D	lge., micro. shift corner Bldg.	—	—	.25	1.00

LINCOLN CENTS

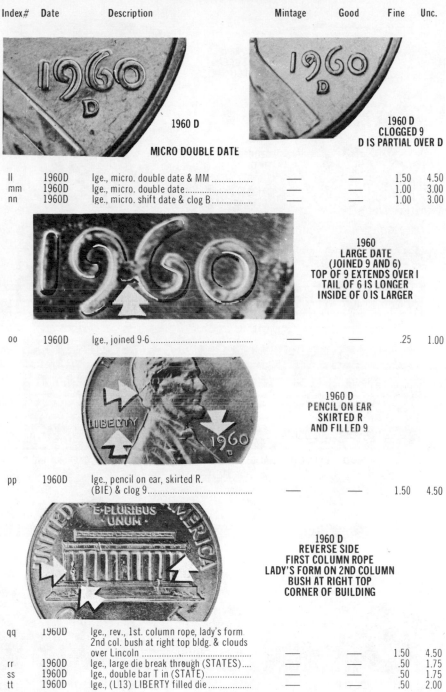

Index#	Date	Description	Mintage	Good	Fine	Unc.

1960 D

MICRO DOUBLE DATE

1960 D
CLOGGED 9
D IS PARTIAL OVER D

Index#	Date	Description	Mintage	Good	Fine	Unc.
ll	1960D	lge., micro. double date & MM	—	—	1.50	4.50
mm	1960D	lge., micro. double date	—	—	1.00	3.00
nn	1960D	lge., micro. shift date & clog B	—	—	1.00	3.00

1960
LARGE DATE
(JOINED 9 AND 6)
TOP OF 9 EXTENDS OVER I
TAIL OF 6 IS LONGER
INSIDE OF 0 IS LARGER

| oo | 1960D | lge., joined 9-6 | — | — | .25 | 1.00 |

1960 D
PENCIL ON EAR
SKIRTED R
AND FILLED 9

| pp | 1960D | lge., pencil on ear, skirted R. (BIE) & clog 9 | — | — | 1.50 | 4.50 |

1960 D
REVERSE SIDE
FIRST COLUMN ROPE
LADY'S FORM ON 2ND COLUMN
BUSH AT RIGHT TOP
CORNER OF BUILDING

qq	1960D	lge., rev., 1st. column rope, lady's form. 2nd col. bush at right top bldg. & clouds over Lincoln	—	—	1.50	4.50
rr	1960D	lge., large die break through (STATES)	—	—	.50	1.75
ss	1960D	lge., double bar T in (STATE)	—	—	.50	1.75
tt	1960D	lge., (L13) LIBERTY filled die	—	—	.50	2.00

LINCOLN CENTS

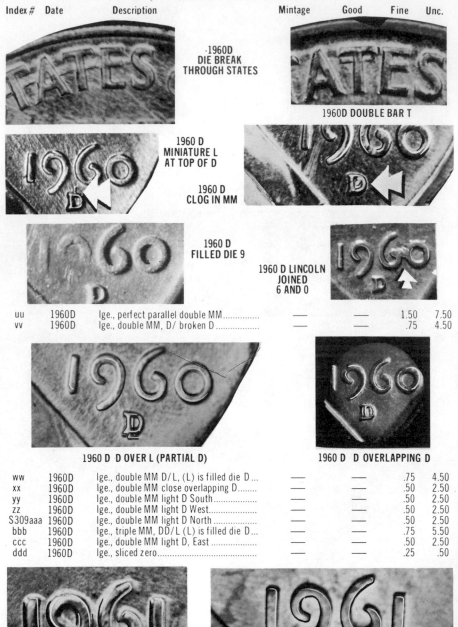

·1960D
DIE BREAK
THROUGH STATES

1960D DOUBLE BAR T

1960 D
MINIATURE L
AT TOP OF D

1960 D
CLOG IN MM

1960 D
FILLED DIE 9

1960 D LINCOLN
JOINED
6 AND 0

Index #	Date	Description	Mintage	Good	Fine	Unc.
uu	1960D	lge., perfect parallel double MM	—	—	1.50	7.50
vv	1960D	lge., double MM, D/ broken D	—	—	.75	4.50

1960 D D OVER L (PARTIAL D)

1960 D D OVERLAPPING D

Index #	Date	Description	Mintage	Good	Fine	Unc.
ww	1960D	lge., double MM D/L, (L) is filled die D	—	—	.75	4.50
xx	1960D	lge., double MM close overlapping D	—	—	.50	2.50
yy	1960D	lge., double MM light D South	—	—	.50	2.50
zz	1960D	lge., double MM light D West	—	—	.50	2.50
S309aaa	1960D	lge., double MM light D North	—	—	.50	2.50
bbb	1960D	lge., triple MM, DD/L (L) is filled die D	—	—	.75	5.50
ccc	1960D	lge., double MM light D, East	—	—	.50	2.50
ddd	1960D	lge., sliced zero	—	—	.25	.50

1961 P LARGE THICK DATE

1961 P SMALL THIN DATE

LINCOLN CENTS

Index #	Date	Description	Mintage	Good	Fine	Unc.
eee	1960D	lge., die break, from T of States through "E" motto	—	—	—	.50
fff	1960D	LIBERTY (right leg of R, die fill)	—	—	—	.50

1961 P
DOT BETWEEN
6 AND 1

1961 D SLANTED LAST 1

S310	1961		756,373,244	—	—	.40
a	1961	thin date	—	—	—	.15
b	1961	thick date	—	—	—	.25
c	1961	slanted first 1	—	—	.25	2.25
d	1961	dot, 196.1	—	—	.25	1.50
e	1961	(BIE)	—	—	.50	1.50
f	1961	(BiE) incomplete	—	—	.50	1.50
g	1961	joined ES in STATES	—	—	.50	1.00
h	1961	joined 9-6	—	—	.50	1.00
i	1961	double lettering on rev.	—	—	.75	1.50
j	1961	various clog parts of LIBERTY	—	—	.40	1.00
k	1961	various clog numbers	—	—	.40	1.00
l	1961	(RHL)	—	—	—	.25
m	1961	(PHL)	—	—	—	.15
n	1961	Bar over US of Trust	—	—	—	.50
o	1961	(RHL) proof	—	—	—	3.00
p	1961	Micro, double date	—	—	1.00	2.50

1961 D MICRO DOUBLE DATE

MICRO DOUBLE DATE AND
MINT MARK

S311	1961D		1,753,266,000	—	—	.10
a	1961D	thin date	—	—	—	.25
b	1961D	thick date	—	—	—	.15
c	1961D	slanted last 1	—	—	.50	1.50
d	1961D	micro. double date	—	—	1.50	4.75
e	1961D	micro. double date & MM	—	—	1.50	4.75
f	1961D	MM, D/I Roman numeral	—	—	.50	2.00
g	1961D	double MM D/L (L) is partial D	—	—	.75	2.50
h	1961D	double MM D over Horizontal D	—	—	1.50	3.50

1961 D
FISH HOOK 9

1961 D
DOUBLE D

D OVER
HORIZONTAL D

LINCOLN CENTS

Index #	Date	Description	Mintage	Good	Fine	Unc.
i	1961D	fish hook 9	—	—	1.50	3.50
j	1961D	double UNITED STATES OF AMERICA	—	—	2.00	4.50
k	1961D	micro. double right upper part of Bldg.	—	—	.75	1.50

1961 D RECUT ONE CENT

1961 D DOUBLE PROFILE ON NECK

l	1961D	micro. double ONE CENT	—	—	2.00	4.50
m	1961D	double profile of neck	—	—	.20	.40

TEARDROP T

1961 D HORNED T

n	1961D	(BIE)	—	—	.50	2.50
o	1961D	dot, 196.1	—	—	.25	1.00
p	1961D	joined 9-6	—	—	.25	.90
q	1961D	(RHL)	—	—	—	.25
r	1961D	(PHL)	—	—	—	.10
s	1961D	various clog parts of LIBERTY	—	—	.25	.75
t	1961D	various clog numbers	—	—	.25	.75
u	1961D	slanted y, of LIBERTY	—	—	.25	.75
v	1961D	r961	—	—	.35	1.00
w	1961D	horned T in LIBERTY	—	—	.25	.75
x	1961D	teardrop T of CENTS	—	—	.25	.75
y	1961D	crack skull, skirted R	—	—	.25	.75
z	1961D	stemmed MM	—	—	.25	.75
S311aa	1961D	Dot under 1st leg of R	—	—	.25	.75

1962 FROSTED LINCOLN

1962 CROSS IN DATE

S312	1962		609,263,000	—	—	.10
a	1962	cross in date, die br. horiz. in 1	—	—	—	.50
b	1962	thin date	—	—	—	.20
c	1962	thick date	—	—	—	.10
d	1962	(BIE)	—	—	—	1.00
e	1962	micro. double date	—	—	.75	1.50
f	1962	(RHL)	—	—	—	.25
g	1962	(PHL)	—	—	—	.10
h	1962	various clog parts of LIBERTY	—	—	—	.75
i	1962	various clog numbers	—	—	—	.75
j	1962	(proof) frosted gem effigy and lettering	—	—	—	3.50
k	1962	(RHL) proof	—	—	—	2.50
S313	1962D		1,793,148,000	—	—	.10
a	1962D	long Y, extended die br. bottom of Y of LIBERTY	—	—	.50	1.50

44

LINCOLN CENTS

Index #	Date	Description	Mintage	Good	Fine	Unc.

1962 D
LONG Y

1962 MICRO
D MINT MARK

Index #	Date	Description	Mintage	Good	Fine	Unc.
b	1962D	double MM, D/L (L) is partial D	—	—	.75	2.50
c	1962D	double MM, light D West	—	—	.50	2.00
d	1962D	triple MM, DD/C (C) is partial D	—	—	1.00	4.50
e	1962D	double 2, and MM	—	—	.75	2.50
f	1962D	micro. MM	—	—	—	.35
g	1962D	various clog parts of LIBERTY	—	—	—	.75
h	1962D	thin date	—	—	—	.20
i	1962D	thick date	—	—	—	.10
j	1962D	micro. double date & MM, clog 9	—	—	1.00	4.75
k	1962D	(RHL)	—	—	—	.20
l	1962D	(PHL)	—	—	—	.10
m	1962D	double profile	—	—	—	1.00
n	1962D	Club 1	—	—	—	.50
o	1962D	various clog numbers	—	—	—	.75
p	1962D	stemmed MM	—	—	—	.75
q	1962D	cross in date, horiz. die br.	—	—	—	.75
r	1962D	goatee chin	—	—	—	.50
s	1962D	lamination type	—	—	—	—

DOT W•E

S 1962 D
LAMINATION TYPE

Index #	Date	Description	Mintage	Good	Fine	Unc.
S314	1963		757,185,000	—	—	.10
a	1963	thin date	—	—	—	.20
b	1963	thick date	—	—	—	.10
c	1963	W•E dot (we)	—	—	—	1.25

POINTED
HAIRLINE

ROUNDED
HAIRLINE

Rounded Hairline (RHL) Proof Cents

A survey showed the RHL variety is in a minority quantity in comparison to the PHL.

It's my opinion the RHL is the result of a different master die hub, and not the result of a filled die. A further study showed both varieties exist in most other dates and proof sets. As these varieties are reported to me I will list for the future editions.

Index #	Date	Description	Mintage	Good	Fine	Unc.
d	1963	(RHL)	—	—	—	.25
e	1963	(PHL)	—	—	—	.10
f	1963	various clog parts of LIBERTY	—	—	—	.50
g	1963	various clog numbers	—	—	—	.50
h	1963	(RHL) Proof	—	—	—	3.00

LINCOLN CENTS

Index#	Date	Description	Mintage	Good	Fine	Unc.
S315	1963D	....	1,774,020,000	—	—	.10
a	1963D	thin date..		—	—	.20
b	1963D	thick date...		—	—	.10
c	1963D	(RHL)...		—	—	.25
d	1963D	(PHL)...		—	—	.10
e	1963D	3/3 in date...		—	.75	4.75
f	1963D	(RHL), recut T in LIBERTY, club shape l		—	—	1.00
g	1963D	double MM. close overlap....................		—	—	.50
h	1963D	double profile.....................................		—	—	.50
i	1963D	micro. double date..............................		—	—	1.00
j	1963D	scallop edge.......................................		—	—	1.00
S316	1964	....		—	—	.10
a	1964	(RHL)...		—	—	.20
b	1964	(PHL)...		—	—	.10
c	1964	(RHL) Proof..		—	—	3.00
d	1964	double "T" in LIBERTY		—	—	.50
e	1964	Frosted (Proof)		—	—	3.75

1964 D
FILLED DIE
ST-TES

Index#	Date	Description	Mintage	Good	Fine	Unc.
S317	1964D	....		—	—	.10
a	1964D	diagonal die break under "E" LIBERTY....		—	—	.40
b	1964D	micro. double profile, date & MM............		—	—	1.50
c	1964D	(RHL)...		—	—	.20
d	1964D	(PHL)...		—	—	.10
e	1964D	MM, touching 9..................................		—	—	.25
f	1964D	large diagonal die break, top of head down to LIBERTY		—	—	.50
g	1964D	thin hairline MM		—	—	.20
h	1964D	clash die varieties...............................		—	—	1.00
i	1964D	micro shift rev. letters.........................		—	—	2.50
j	1964D	clash die, no dot after "unum"		—	—	4.50
k	1964D	missing wall right top bldg.		—	—	1.50
l	1964D	missing neck......................................		—	—	1.50
m	1964D	various blobs, parts rev. or obv.		—	—	.75
n	1964D	micro double (Cent) & bldg..................		—	—	3.50
o	1964D	various position MM		—	—	—
p	1964D	filled die (St-tes)		—	—	1.50
q	1964D	dot under 4, crack skull........................		—	—	1.50
S317-5	1965	....		—	—	.10
a	1965	RHL..		—	—	.15
b	1965	joined EN (top) Cents..........................		—	—	.50
c	1965	clash dies..		—	—	2.50
d	1965	various blobs columns, rev.		—	—	.50
e	1965	Lincoln speaks (5 blobs at mouth)..........		—	—	13.50
f	1965	rotated die rev. 15 degrees...................		—	—	1.50
g	1965	feather under T (Liberty)		—	—	9.50
h	1965	double dot left of ..unum......................		—	—	25.00
i	1965	micro double date................................		—	—	2.00
j	1965	dot over 0 (one)..................................		—	—	1.50
k	1965	dot over N (cents)		—	—	1.50
l	1965	no dot after (unum)..............................		—	—	2.50
m	1965	pine tree/FG (initials) - clash dies		—	—	10.00
n	1965	slant line in 0 (God).............................		—	—	1.00
o	1965	micro y in (Liberty)		—	—	.50
p	1965	missing right wall top of bldg.................		—	—	1.50

LINCOLN CENTS

Index #	Date	Description	Mintage	Good	Fine	Unc.
q	1965	various bubbles on obv...........................	—	—	—	1.00
r	1965	club 1 in date....................................	—	—	—	1.00
s	1965	long cont. bust over rim	—	—	—	1.50
S317-6	1966	....	—	—	—	.10
a	1966	micro double "cents" rev.......................	—	—	—	3.00
b	1966	button, right lapel out of line, RHL	—	—	—	1.50
c	1966	cross in date, blob dot under M of America....................................	—	—	—	2.50
d	1966	club 1 in date....................................	—	—	—	.50
e	1966	micro dots near (Unum)........................	—	—	—	.50

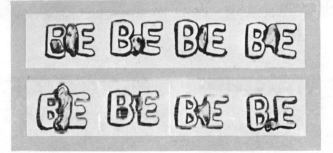

(BIE) CLOGGED TYPES

TYPE I
1960/1960 Proof LD/SD
"BER" especially doubled

TYPE I
1960/1960 PROOF LARGE OVER SMALL DATE
CENT (Small Date centered underneath Large
Date)

TYPE II
1960/1960 Proof SD/LD
"BER" especially doubled

TYPE II
1960/1960 PROOF LARGE OVER SMALL DATE
CENT (Small Date centered on top of Large Date)

TYPE III
1960/1960 Proof LD/SD
"Y" especially doubled

TYPE III
1960/1960 PROOF LARGE OVER SMALL DATE
CENT (Small Date off-center underneath Large
Date)

Early Die State (Called "Type I")
1960/1960 D/D LARGE OVER SMALL DATE
CENT (Small Date centered on top of Large
Date) Early die state = no die break lump in "6"
= 9% to 10% of 1960/1960 D/D
(s309e)

Late Die State (Called "Type II")
1960/1960 D/D LARGE OVER SMALL DATE
CENT Late die state = die break lump in "6"
(also die scratch from "1" in date and lump
on tip of "9") = with lump in 6: 90% to 91%
of all 1960/1960 D/D (S309e)

TWO CENT PIECES 1864-1873

Index #	Date	Description	Mintage	Good	Fine	Unc.

1865
DIEBREAK
BOTTOM OF E
TO TOP OF R
IN AMERICA

1864

SMALL MOTTO
T IS CLOSE TO RIBBON
STEM ON LEAF

This issue is the first coin to contain the motto "In God We Trust." The 1864 has two varieties of the motto, the large and the small. The small motto has a stem at the edge of a leaf near the ribbon bearing the word "WE." The letter T of TRUST just touches fold of ribbon. The large motto has the T of TRUST about 1/32" spaced away from ribbon edge, the leaf has no stem.

Index—	Date	Description	Mintage	Good	Fine	Unc.
S318	1864	large motto	19,847,000	1.50	3.50	18.00
a	1864	small motto	—	35.00	60.00	250.00
b	1864	double date	—	4.50	14.00	40.00
c	1864	double 18	—	3.50	8.50	30.00
d	1864	double 1	—	2.75	5.75	24.00
e	1864	small motto Double U. S. America	—	45.00	70.00	300.00
S319	1865		13,640,000	1.50	3.50	24.00
a	1865	double date	—	4.50	18.00	75.00
b	1865	clash die, outline of obv. on rcv.	—	1.75	5.50	26.50
c	1865	die break connected E-R of AMERICA	—	1.75	5.50	26.00
d	1865	round 8 cutetip bar 5, knob 6	—	—	—	—
e	1865	barrel 8 curve bar 5, square knob 6	—	—	—	—
S320	1866		3,177,000	1.75	4.50	25.00
S321	1867		2,938,000	1.75	4.50	27.00

1867
RECUT
MOTTO

1871 DOUBLE MOTTO

a	1867	double motto & legend	—	7.00	18.00	40.00
b	1867	double date	—	7.00	18.00	40.00
c	1867	double 1	—	2.75	7.50	30.00
S322	1868		2,803,000	1.75	5.00	30.00
S323	1869		1,546,000	3.00	6.00	29.00
a	1869	recut 69	—	4.50	10.00	45.00
S324	1870		861,000	4.00	8.50	40.00
S325	1871		721,000	5.75	12.50	48.00
a	1871	recut 18	—	6.50	13.00	53.00
b	1871	double date	—	9.00	20.00	60.00
c	1871	double motto	—	9.00	20.00	60.00
S326	1872		65,000	32.00	48.00	115.00
S327	1873	open 3 proofs only	PROOFS		$700.00	
a	1873	closed 3 proofs only	PROOFS		$700.00	

THREE CENT PIECES (NICKEL) 1865-1889

Index #	Date	Description	Mintage	Good	Fine	Unc.

OBVERSE

REVERSE

Composition is 75% copper and 25% nickel

Index #	Date	Description	Mintage	Good	Fine	Unc.
S328	1865		11,382,000	1.75	3.00	17.00
a	1865	clash die, out line	—	2.00	4.00	15.00
b	1865	last A, in AMERICA, recut	—	2.00	4.00	15.00
c	1865	Double Date, shifted N.E.	—	17.00	55.00	100.00
S329	1866		4,800,000	1.75	3.50	17.00
a	1866	recut last 6	—	3.00	6.75	20.00
b	1866	recut UNITED STATES AMERICA		2.50	5.50	16.00
c	1866	clash die, obv. outline shown on rev. (due to press operated without blank planchet between dies)	—	2.75	6.50	18.00
S330	1867		3,915,000	1.75	3.50	17.00
S331	1868		3,252,000	1.75	3.50	17.00
a	1868	recut 68	—	5.00	8.75	28.00
b	1868	clash dies	—	2.00	4.00	15.00
S332	1869		1,604,000	1.75	3.50	17.00
a	1869	double Roman III	—	2.00	5.50	14.00
b	1869	9/9	—	5.50	18.00	45.00
c	1869	double date	—	9.00	26.00	75.00
S333	1870		1,335,000	2.50	5.50	18.00
a	1870	repunch 1870 over small date	—	rare	—	—
S334	1871		604,000	4.75	9.50	30.00
S335	1872		862,000	4.50	9.00	28.00

OPEN 3

CLOSED 3

1882 HEAVY 2

Index #	Date	Description	Mintage	Good	Fine	Unc.
S336	1873	open 3 all kinds	1,173,000	2.00	7.00	18.00
a	1873	closed 3	—	2.50	7.50	19.00
S337	1874		790,000	4.00	9.00	30.00
a	1874	recut U.S. AMERICA	—	4.50	10.00	30.00
S338	1875		228,000	6.00	14.00	39.00
a	1875	(Dot) 18.75	—	7.00	16.00	55.00
S338x	1876		162,000	5.00	14.00	37.00
S339	1877	proofs only	625	PROOFS $750.00		
S340	1878	proofs only	2,350	PROOFS 225.00		
S341	1879		41,200	5.00	10.00	30.00
S342	1880		24,900	6.00	11.50	32.00
S343	1881		1,080,500	2.75	7.50	19.00
S344	1882		25,300	5.50	14.00	34.00
a	1882	heavy 2	—	5.75	15.00	35.00
S345	1883		10,600	7.00	15.00	36.00
S346	1884		5,640	8.00	16.00	40.00
S347	1885		3,790	8.50	17.00	41.00
S348	1886	proofs only	4,290	PROOFS $75.00		
S349	1887		7,960	18.00	30.00	100.00
a	1887/86	overdate proofs only	—	PROOFS $225.00		
S350	1888		41,080	6.50	14.00	35.00
S351	1889		21,560	7.00	15.00	36.50

THREE CENT PIECES (SILVER) 1851-1873

Index #	Date	Description	Mintage	Good	Fine	Unc.

This issue is the smallest of the U.S. issues, made of silver. It's smaller than an ordinary dime and recognized by the "Star" on obverse and large "C" with Roman numeral III on the reverse. Choice specimens of uncirculated and proofs are scarce.

Index #	Date	Description	Mintage	Good	Fine	Unc.
S352	1851		5,447,000	4.75	8.50	40.00
S353	18510		720,000	12.00	29.00	95.00
a	18510	double U. S. A.	—	13.00	31.00	100.00
S354	1852		18,663,000	2.50	8.00	35.00
a	1852	clash dies	—	2.75	9.00	37.00
b	1852	recut date	—	3.00	11.00	45.00
S355	1853		11,400,000	3.00	8.00	30.00
S356	1854	three outlines to star	671,000	8.00	16.00	45.00
a	1854	18554, light 5 between 8-5	—	RARE		
S357	1855		139,000	12.00	40.00	120.00
a	1855	recut 55's	—	14.00	45.00	130.00
S358	1856		1,458,000	8.00	14.00	55.00
S359	1857		1,042,000	7.00	13.00	50.00
S360	1858		1,604,000	6.00	11.00	44.00
S361	1859	two outlines to star	365,000	8.50	13.00	35.00
S362	1860		287,000	8.50	13.00	36.00
S363	1861		498,000	8.00	11.00	32.00
a	1861	recut date	—	10.00	10.00	36.00
b	1861	double stars	—	8.50	12.00	37.00
S364	1862		363,500	8.00	12.00	32.00
a	1862	1862/61 overdate	—	12.50	18.00	50.00
S365	1863		21,460	27.00	49.00	130.00
a	1863	1863/2 overdate	—	RARE		
S366	1864		470	—	—	200.00
S367	1865		8,500	PROOF		200.00

Most coins issued from 1863 to 1872 were melted or exported more proofs are known to exist than circulated coins.

Index #	Date	Description	Mintage	Good	Fine	Unc.
S368	1866		22,725	PROOF		120.00
S369	1867		4,625	PROOF		120.00
a	1867	double date	—	RARE		
S370	1868		4,100	PROOF		150.00
S371	1869		5,100	PROOF		125.00
a	1869	double date	—	RARE		
b	1869	recut 69	—	RARE		
S372	1870		4,000	PROOF		125.00
S373	1871		4,260	PROOF		125.00
S374	1872		1,950	PROOF		125.00
S375	1873	close 3	000	PROOF		225.00

SHIELD NICKELS 1866-1883

1867
SHIELD
NICKEL

1866 SHIELD
NICKEL WITH RAYS

Two types were issued during 1866-1867 "Rays" and "Without Rays"

Index #	Date	Description	Mintage	Good	Fine	Unc.
S376	1866	(rays) all types	14,742,000	4.50	13.00	95.00
a	1866	(no rays) rare	—	VERY RARE		
b	1866	repunch 66/66	—	16.00	40.00	105.00
c	1866	extra punch 6, 18666	—	18.00	50.00	110.00
d	1866	small date, lg. motto	—	6.75	16.00	100.00
e	1866	large date, sm. motto	—	6.75	16.00	100.00
f	1866	Double Date, 1st cut very high	—	VERY RARE		
g	1866	double date north	—	12.00	25.00	85.00
h	1866	double date south	—	12.00	25.00	85.00
S377	1867	(no rays) common	30,909,000	2.00	5.50	24.00
a	1867	(rays) rare	—	9.50	28.00	110.00
b	1867	double date, rays	—	12.50	45.00	150.00
c	1867	1/1, no rays	—	3.50	7.50	30.00
d	1867	double IN GOD WE TRUST	—	3.50	7.00	28.00
e	1867	recut date (Rays)	—	8.50	40.00	140.00
f	1867	triple date	—	—	65.00	165.00
g	1867	repunched date	—	rare	—	—

1867
DOUBLE
DATE

1882
DOUBLE
DATE

S378	1868		28,817,000	2.00	7.00	28.00
a	1868	double date, repunch 1868/68	—	8.50	18.00	47.00
b	1868	type 1, type of 1867 lg. stars	—	3.00	6.00	28.00
c	1868	type 2, small stars	—	3.00	6.00	28.00
S379	1869		16,395,000	2.50	8.00	29.00
a	1869	1869/8	—	7.00	15.00	40.00
b	1869	type 1, of 1867 lg. stars	—	3.25	6.50	28.00
c	1869	type 2, small stars	—	3.25	6.50	28.00
d	1869	Die Break through bottom of date	—	3.25	6.50	28.00
e	1869	double date	—	12.00	27.00	90.00
S380	1870		4,806,000	3.75	9.50	38.00
S381	1871		561,000	35.00	52.00	175.00
S382	1872		6,036,000	3.75	8.00	32.00
a	1872	double date, shifted shield	rare	—	—	—

SHIELD NICKELS

1882 EXTRA PIECE AT END OF 2

1883/2

Index #	Date	Description	Mintage	Good	Fine	Unc.
S383	1873	open 3 all type	4,550,000	5.00	8.50	42.00
a	1873	closed 3	—	5.50	9.00	44.00
b	1873	closed 3 recut date	—	7.00	15.00	51.00
S384	1874		3,538,000	7.50	13.00	45.00
a	1874	Double date	—	9.50	18.00	60.00
S385	1875		2,097,000	13.00	27.00	100.00
S386	1876		2,530,000	7.00	14.00	47.00
S387	1877	proofs	500	PROOF	$1000.00	
S388	1878	proofs	2,350	PROOF	$275.00	
S389	1879		29,100	14.00	20.00	75.00
a	1879	Recut 9	—	15.00	23.00	75.00
S390	1880		19,995	15.00	23.00	75.00
S391	1881		72,373	12.00	18.00	60.00
S392	1882		11,476,600	2.75	5.75	28.00
a	1882	double date & motto	—	11.00	18.00	55.00
b	1882	double date 1882/1882	—	10.00	16.00	49.00
c	1882	heavy 2	—	2.75	5.75	23.00
d	1882	extra piece end of 2	—	2.75	5.75	23.00
e	1882	1882/1	—	26.00	90.00	150.00
S393	1883		1,456,919	2.50	6.00	26.00
a	1883	1883/2	—	26.00	75.00	175.00
b	1883	double date shifted north	—	12.00	26.00	37.00

LIBERTY HEAD NICKELS 1883-1912

OBVERSE

REVERSE

Two types were used during 1883, one with the word CENTS, on the reverse side at the bottom, and one type without the word CENTS. While the issue lists the with CENTS type at a greater amount than the type without CENTS it is scarce. It is believed the without CENTS type was hoarded as a first issue, the second type with CENTS probably melted. It is believed the reason for adding the word CENTS was because the Liberty nickel resembled a $5.00 gold piece when gold plated and passed as such, thus the adding of word CENTS.

The 1913 Liberty nickel wasn't an official issue, however, it is a popular and rare coin among collectors.

S394	1883	no "CENTS" (N.C.)	5,479,000	.75	1.50	8.00
a	1883	11 stars filled die	—	2.50	5.75	9.00
b	1883	10 stars	—	2.50	5.75	9.00
c	1883	double date & lettering	—	4.75	11.50	30.00
d	1883	double motto "E PLURIBUS UNUM"	—	1.00	3.75	8.50
e	1883	double STATES	—	1.00	3.75	8.50
f	1883	die break through "E PLU" double U.S. OF AMERICA	—	1.50	4.50	11.50

LIBERTY HEAD NICKELS

Index #	Date	Description	Mintage	Good	Fine	Unc.
g	1883	STATES, (dot)	—	1.00	3.00	8.50
h	1883	1/1883	—	2.00	5.25	10.00
i	1883	18/1883	—	3.00	8.50	12.50
j	1883	1883/8 (1st 8)	—	1.50	4.50	9.50
k	1883	racketeer nickel, reeded edge, gold plated man made to resemble a $5.00 gold piece	—	1.50	3.75	15.00
l	1883	with "CENTS"	16,032,000	4.75	9.50	35.00
S395	1884		11,273,000	5.00	11.00	40.00

1884 DOUBLE

1913 LIBERTY HEAD NICKEL

Index #	Date	Description	Mintage	Good	Fine	Unc.
a	1884	1/1884 (Proof $175.00)	—	9.00	21.00	75.00
S396	1885		1,476,000	55.00	90.00	275.00
S397	1886		3,330,000	30.00	50.00	125.00
S398	1887		15,263,000	3.25	6.00	35.00
S399	1888		10,720,000	6.50	9.50	35.00
S400	1889		15,881,000	2.75	5.75	35.00
S401	1890		16,259,000	2.50	8.50	34.00
S402	1891		16,834,000	2.00	6.50	30.00
S403	1892		11,699,000	2.50	7.00	32.00
a	1892	8 stars, filled die	—	3.75	9.50	47.00
S404	1893		13,370,000	2.00	5.75	32.00
S405	1894		5,413,000	5.00	11.00	40.00
S406	1895		9,979,000	2.00	5.25	30.00
S407	1896		8,842,000	2.00	8.50	50.00
S408	1897		20,428,000	.75	3.50	29.00
S409	1898		12,532,000	.75	3.50	29.00
S410	1899		26,000,000	.60	3.00	25.00
S411	1900		27,255,000	.50	2.00	24.00
S412	1901		26,480,000	.50	2.00	22.00
a	1901	1901/1	—	2.75	8.50	30.00
S413	1902		31,480,000	.40	2.00	21.00
S414	1903		28,006,000	.40	2.00	21.00
a	1903	upright reverse—complete rotated die	—	2.50	6.00	40.00
S415	1904		21,404,000	.40	2.00	20.00
a	1904	1/1904	—	2.50	6.75	22.00
S416	1905		29,827,000	.40	2.00	20.00
S417	1906		38,613,000	.40	2.00	20.00
S418	1907		39,214,000	.40	2.00	20.00
S419	1908		22,686,000	.40	2.00	20.00
S420	1909		11,590,000	.50	2.25	22.00
S421	1910		30,169,000	.40	2.50	18.00
S422	1911		39,559,000	.40	2.50	18.00
S423	1912		26,236,000	.40	2.50	18.00
S424	1912D		8,474,000	1.50	5.75	195.00
a	1912D	Double MM, dot & cents	—	3.50	18.50	250.00
S425	1912S		238,000	28.00	52.00	380.00
a	1912S	Double MM & United	—	45.00	75.00	450.00
S426	1913	(not a regular issue) popular & rare	(5)		$29,000.00	

Index #	Date	Description	Mintage	Good	Fine	Unc.

1913
DOUBLE
PROFILE

1916
DOUBLE
DATE

The Indian shown is the model of (3) chiefs

The buffalo on the reverse is actually a "Bison" modeled after the bison "Black Diamond" in the New York Zoological Gardens.

Index #	Date	Description	Mintage	Good	Fine	Unc.
S427	1913	type 1 (on the mound)	30,993,000	1.00	2.50	10.50
a	1913	double profile	—	1.50	4.75	14.00
b	1913	double date	—	3.00	8.00	20.00
c	1913	type 2 (on the plane)	29,858,000	1.00	3.50	12.00
d	1913	double date	—	4.00	9.50	25.00
e	1913	Let. Chin	—	1.00	4.00	14.00

CLASHED DIE LETTERS UNDER CHIN

Press struck without a planchet in die. Impression was superimposed on obverse side of die resulting in motto under chin of Indian. " E PLURIBUS UNUM" Bumps, part of Buffalo appear on obverse.

Index #	Date	Description	Mintage	Good	Fine	Unc.
S428	1913D	type 1	5,337,000	3.50	6.00	24.00
a	1913D	type 2 (on the plane)	4,156,000	16.00	30.00	80.00
S429	1913S	type 1 (on the mound)	2,105,000	5.00	10.00	36.00
a	1913S	type 2 (on the plane)	1,209,000	30.00	40.00	115.00
S430	1914		20,665,000	1.00	3.50	21.00
a	1914	letter chin, (clashed dies)	—	1.00	4.00	23.00
b	1914	double date & profile	—	4.00	12.50	50.00
S431	1914D		3,912,000	15.00	28.00	100.00
a	1914D	IVE CENTS, fill die	—	16.00	29.00	105.00
S432	1914S		3,470,000	3.50	9.00	65.00
S433	1915		20,987,000	1.00	3.25	21.00
a	1915	two leathers, (fill die)	—	2.00	6.50	25.00
b	1915	double date	—	4.00	12.00	50.00
S434	1915D		7,567,000	3.50	10.00	60.00
a	1915D	letter chin, (clashed dies)	—	4.50	10.00	60.00
S435	1915S		1,505,000	7.00	17.00	100.00
a	1915S	let. chin	—	9.50	20.00	105.00
S436	1916		63,498,000	.50	2.00	15.00
a	1916	double date, shift north	—	16.00	50.00	200.00
b	1916	two feathers, fill die	—	2.75	6.00	21.00
S437	1916D		13,333,000	2.75	6.75	60.00
a	1916D	double, LIBERTY	—	3.50	9.00	65.00
b	1916D	let. chin	—	4.00	9.00	75.00
S438	1916S		11,860,000	2.50	6.75	60.00
a	1916S	let chin	—	2.75	8.00	65.00
S439	1917		51,424,000	.50	2.00	16.00
a	1917	two feathers	—	2.00	6.00	19.00
S440	1917D		9,910,000	2.00	9.00	85.00
S441	1917S		4,193,000	3.00	11.00	120.00
S442	1918		32,086,000	.50	1.50	38.50
a	1918	let. chin	—	1.00	2.50	40.00
S443	1918D		8,362,000	3.00	9.50	160.00
a	1918D/7	overdate, rare	—	125.00	375.00	3750.00
b	1918D	double LIBERTY	—	4.00	13.00	180.00

Index #	Date	Description	Mintage	Good	Fine	Unc.

1916 BUFFALO

1938 D DOUBLE PARALLEL D

Index #	Date	Description	Mintage	Good	Fine	Unc.
S444	1918S		4,882,000	2.75	9.00	180.00
a	1918S	let. chin	—	5.00	12.00	160.00
b	1918S	double profile	—	5.50	15.00	160.00
S445	1919		60,868,000	.35	1.25	19.00
a	1919	"FI—" filled die (FIVE)	—	1.50	3.75	22.00
b	1919	let. chin	—	1.00	2.50	21.00
S446	1919D		8,006,000	3.00	13.00	185.00
S447	1919S		7.521.000	2.75	11.00	195.00
a	1919S	let. chin	—	4.50	16.00	165.00
S448	1920		63,093,000	.50	1.00	21.00
a	1920	"FIV" fill die (FIVE)	—	1.25	3.00	19.00
b	1920	let. chin	—	1.00	2.75	19.00
c	1920	—20 fill date var.	—	2.00	4.50	21.00
S449	1920D		9,418,000	2.50	9.50	185.00
a	1920D	let. chin	—	3.00	11.00	165.00
b	1920D	two feathers	—	3.50	12.00	170.00
S450	1920S		9.689.000	2.00	8.00	160.00
a	1920S	let. chin	—	2.75	11.00	165.00
b	1920S	double profile	—	3.75	16.00	195.00
S451	1921		10.663.000	.60	3.00	42.00
a	1921	let. chin	—	1.00	2.75	40.00
b	1921	die br.. PLURIBUS	—	1.00	2.50	37.00
c	1921	two feathers	—	3.75	13.00	165.00
S452	1921S		1.557.000	9.50	25.00	260.00
S453	1923		35.715.000	.40	1.00	20.00
a	1923	let. chin	—	1.00	2.50	17.00
S454	1923S		6.142.000	1.50	7.00	145.00
a	1923S	let. chin	—	3.00	9.50	150.00
S455	1924		21.620.000	.30	1.00	15.00
a	1924	let. chin	—	.75	2.50	18.00
S456	1924D		5.258.000	2.00	6.00	160.00
S457	1924S		1.437,000	5.00	16.00	600.00
a	1924S	let. chin	—	7.00	24.00	260.00
S458	1925		35.565.000	.30	.90	21.00
a	1925	let. chin	—	1.00	2.50	22.00
S459	1925D		4,450,000	6.00	13.00	185.00
a	1925D	let. chin	—	7.00	17.00	145.00
S460	1925S		6.256.000	4.00	8.50	220.00
a	1925S	let. chin	—	4.00	12.50	195.00
b	1925S	missing neck.	—	4.00	12.00	190.00
c	1925S	two feathers	—	4.00	13.00	190.00
S461	1926		44,693,000	.35	.75	16.00
S462	1926D		5,638,000	2.75	9.00	270.00
S463	1926S		970,000	5.00	18.00	375.00
a	1926S	clash dies	—	6.00	24.00	350.00
S464	1927		37,981,000	.25	.75	13.00
S465	1927D		5,730,000	1.50	4.00	42.00
S466	1927S		3.430,000	1.50	9.00	260.00
a	1927S	two feathers	—	3.50	15.00	260.00
S467	1928		23.411,000	.25	.75	13.00
S468	1928D		6,436,000	.50	1.75	15.00
a	1928D	double profile & date	—	2.50	6.00	28.00
S469	1928S		6,936,000	.50	1.50	50.00

BUFFALO NICKELS

Index #	Date	Description	Mintage	Good	Fine	Unc.
S470	1929	....	36,446,000	.25	.75	11.00
S471	1929D	....	8,370.000	.35	1.25	15.00
a	1929D	double MM....................	—	1.00	4.50	18.00
S472	1929S	....	7,754,000	.35	1.25	14.00
a	1929S	double LIBERTY....................	—	2.00	6.00	17.00
b	1929S	two feathers....................	—	1.50	4.75	15.00
S473	1930	....	22,849,000	.25	.85	12.00
S474	1930S	....	5,435,000	.40	1.75	35.00
a	1930S	8 legs, rev. side....................	—	16.50	50.00	110.00
b	1930S	double MM shift West....................	—	18.00	54.00	
S475	1931S	....	1,200,000	3.75	6.50	60.00
S476	1934	....	20,213,000	.25	.70	9.50
S477	1934D	....	7,480,000	.40	1.50	14.00

**1935-P
TWO-LEGGED
BUFFALO**

Index #	Date	Description	Mintage	Good	Fine	Unc.
S478	1935	....	58,264,000	.20	.35	5.00
a	1935	double date....................	—	2.00	7.00	14.00
b	1935	two legged	—		RARE	
S479	1935D	....	12,092,000	.20	.50	10.00
S480	1935S	....	10,300,000	.20	.50	8.50
a	1935S	Double MM	—	9.50	17.00	40.00
S481	1936	....	119,001,000	.20	.40	5.50
a	1936	two legs, (fill die)....................	—	15.00	50.00	110.00
b	1936	FIV (FIVE) fill die....................	—	1.00	2.50	9.00
S482	1936D	....	24,418,000	.25	.50	4.50
S483	1936S	....	14,930,000	.25	.50	6.50
a	1936S	double MM....................	—	14.00	32.00	85.00
S484	1937	....	79,485,000	.20	.40	4.50
a	1937	dot above V in (FIVE)....................	—	1.00	3.50	9.50
S485	1937D	....	17,826,000	.20	.50	5.00
a	1937D	double profile & date....................	—	3.00	9.50	28.00
b	1937D	3 legged, fill die....................	—	30.00	60.00	210.00

**1937D
RIGHT FRONT
LEG MISSING**

**1938 D
DOUBLE D OVER S**

note: only hoof shows, beware of alteration if complete leg gone.

Index #	Date	Description	Mintage	Good	Fine	Unc.
S486	1937S	....	5,635,000	.20	.50	5.00
a	1937S	double date....................	—	2.75	8.00	22.00
b	1937S	double MM....................	—	2.75	8.00	22.00
S487	1938D	....	7,020,000	.20	.50	4.50
a	1938D	double MM, parallel....................	—	1.50	4.00	15.00
b	1938D	double MM, D/S, center of S in D....................	—	3.50	12.00	65.00
c	1938D	double MM, D/S, same with outline of S....................	—	4.50	15.00	75.00
d	1938D	triple MM, DD/S....................	—	6.50	30.00	110.00

Index #	Date	Description	Mintage	Good	Fine	Unc.

1944.S SPLIT COIN (PIECED TOGETHER)

OBVERSE

INSIDE OF REVERSE

Designed by Felix Schlag, showing portrait of Jefferson, and Jefferson's home "MONTICELLO" on reverse.

Index #	Date	Description	Mintage	Good	Fine	Unc.
S488	1938		19,515,000	.10	.25	3.00
a	1938	Wrinkled forehead	—	.10	.25	4.75
S489	1938D		5,376,000	1.00	2.00	5.50
a	1938D	double MM	—	1.25	3.00	14.00
S490	1938S		4,105,000	1.75	3.50	9.00
S491	1939		120,627,000	.10	.25	2.50
a	1939	re-engraved "MONTICELLO"	—	1.00	2.50	17.00
b	1939	Broken "M" & joined "E" in America, die break/"O" incello	—	.50	1.25	9.50
S492	1939D		3,514,000	4.00	6.00	44.00
S493	1939S		6,630,000	.80	1.50	17.00
a	1939S	double profile & dome	—	1.50	3.75	30.00
b	1939S	large MM	—	—	—	—
c	1939S	small MM	—	—	—	—
S494	1940		176,499,000	—	—	1.50
S495	1940D		43,540,000	—	.25	1.75
a	1940D	bar/zero	—	.25	.50	3.00
S496	1940S		39,690,000	.10	.25	2.75
a	1940S	double MM	—	.50	1.50	4.75
S497	1941		203,283,000	—	—	1.25
S498	1941D		53,432,000	—	.25	1.60
a	1941D	double MM	—	.50	1.00	4.50
S499	1941S		43,445,000	—	.35	2.00
a	1941S	double MM	—	.50	1.00	4.75
b	1941S	triple MM	—	.75	2.25	7.00
c	1941S	large MM	—	—	.35	3.00
d	1941S	small MM	—	—	.35	3.00
S500	1942		49,818,000	—	—	2.50
S501	1942D		13,938,000	.20	.75	12.00
a	1942D	double MM	—	.25	1.00	22.00
b	1942D	D/Horizontal D, Double MM	—	1.00	4.75	30.00

JEFFERSON NICKELS (WAR ISSUE) SILVER

During 1942 the nickel alloy was scarce, in replacing this metal silver was used in the following ratio; 56% copper, 35% silver and 9% manganese. This issue has the mint mark located over the dome of MONTICELLO. It's noted that many of this issue have laminated or peeling layers. This is due to the silver mixture and heating process.

Index #	Date	Description	Mintage	Good	Fine	Unc.
S502	1942P		57,900,000	.25	.50	8.00
a	1942P	double MM	—	.50	1.50	20.00
S503	1942S		32,900,000	—	.40	3.50
a	1942S	flag pole, die br. through MM/dome	—	.25	1.00	7.50
S504	1943		271,165,000	—	.25	2.50
a	1943P	flag pole/dome, die br.	—	—	.50	4.00
b	1943	die br. appears as 3/2 (date)	—	—	1.00	5.00
S505	1943D		15,294,000	.20	1.00	4.00
a	1943D	crack skull	—	—	1.00	6.50

58

JEFFERSON NICKELS

1944P
DIEBREAK
OBVERSE

1945S
FLAG POLE OVER DOME

REVERSE

Index #	Date	Description	Mintage	Good	Fine	Unc.
S506	1943S		104,060,000	—	.35	2.00
a	1943S	flag pole, die br./dome	—	—	.75	4.00
S507	1944P		119,150,000	—	.25	2.75
		1944 nickels without MM, "P" are considered counterfeits	—	—	—	—
a	1944P	flag pole/dome	—	.10	.50	3.75
b	1944P	double MM	—	.50	1.00	5.50
c	1944P	LIB5RTY	—	.50	1.50	6.50
d	1944P	various die br. obv.-rev.	—	—	.50	3.25
S508	1944D		32,309,000	—	.35	2.75
S509	1944S		21,640,000	—	.50	3.75
a	1944S	micro. double date	—	.50	.75	4.25
b	1944S	"QF" die br. (OF AMERICA)	—	.25	.75	4.75
S510	1945P		119,408,000	—	—	3.75
a	1945P	double date	—	.50	2.00	8.50
b	1945P	double MM	—	—	1.50	6.50
c	1945P	double MONTICELLO & CENTS	—	.75	1.50	15.00
S511	1945D		37,158,000	—	—	2.25
S512	1945S		58,939,000	—	—	2.00
a	1945S	flag pole	—	—	.50	4.00
b	1945S	part MM, fill die	—	—	—	3.00
S513	1946		161,116,000	—	—	.90
S514	1946D		45,292,000	—	—	1.25
a	1946D	double MM	—	—	1.00	2.75
S515	1946S		13,560,000	—	—	2.00
a	1946S	double dome	—	—	1.00	4.50
S516	1947		95,000,000	—	—	1.00
a	1947	double profile	—	—	—	1.75
b	1947	dot, 19.47	—	—	1.00	2.00
S517	1947D		37,882,000	—	—	1.50
S518	1947S		24,720,000	—	—	2.00
a	1947S	double profile & date	—	—	1.50	6.50
S519	1948		89,348,000	—	—	.90
S520	1948D		44,734,000	—	—	1.75
a	1948D	double MM	—	.50	1.00	4.50
S522	1948S		11,300,000	.25	.50	3.00
a	1948S	double MM	—	.50	1.00	4.50
S523	1949		60,652,000	—	—	1.50
S524	1949D		35,238,000	—	—	2.00
a	1949D	double profile & MM	—	.50	2.00	7.00
S525	1949S		9,716,000	.25	.65	3.75
a	1949S	double MM	—	.50	1.50	8.00
S526	1950		9,847,000	.20	.50	3.75
S527	1950D		2,630,000	9.00	13.50	16.00
a	1950D	letter edge	—	9.00	13.75	21.00
S528	1951		28,689,000	—	—	1.60
a	1951	double bar 5	—	.50	1.00	4.50
S529	1951D		20,460,000	—	—	2.75
a	1951D	double bar 5	—	.50	1.50	4.75
b	1951D	V nickel, "Star" near date is V	—	.35	1.50	4.95

JEFFERSON NICKELS

Index #	Date	Description	Mintage	Good	Fine	Unc.

1951
DOUBLE
BAR ON 5

1954S
S OVER D

Index #	Date	Description	Mintage	Good	Fine	Unc.
S530	1951S	....	7,776,000	.50	1.50	6.50
S531	1952	....	64,069,000	—	—	.90
S532	1952D	....	30,638,000	—	—	4.50
a	1952D	double MM..................................	—	—	1.50	7.75
S533	1952S	....	20,572,000	—	—	1.50
a	1952S	double MM..................................	—	—	1.50	7.75
S534	1953	....	46,772,000	—	—	.80
S535	1953D	....	59,878,000	—	—	.80
a	1953D	double MM & profile....................	—	—	1.00	3.00
S536	1953S	....	19,210,000	—	—	1.50
a	1953S	double MM & profile....................	—	—	1.25	3.50
S537	1954	....	47,917,000	—	—	.50
a	1954	double profile.............................	—	—	—	1.50
b	1954	double dome...............................	—	—	—	2.00

1954S
MICRO S

LARGE S

Index #	Date	Description	Mintage	Good	Fine	Unc.
S538	1954D	....	117,183,000	—	—	.50
a	1954D	double MM..................................	—	—	.50	1.75
S539	1954S	....	29,384,000	—	.25	.90
a	1954S	double MM & profile....................	—	—	1.00	6.75
b	1954S	micro. MM..................................	—	—	.50	2.00
c	1954S	large MM....................................	—	—	—	1.25
d	1954S	triple MM...................................	—	—	1.50	5.25
e	1954S	double MM, S/D...........................	—	—	3.50	25.00
f	1954S	bar/G (god)................................	—	—	.50	2.50
S540	1955	....	8,266,200	—	1.00	3.50
S541	1955D	....	74,464,000	—	—	.55
a	1955D	double MM..................................	—	—	.50	2.50
b	1955D	double MM, D/S...........................	—	—	1.50	15.00
S542	1956	....	35,885,000	—	—	.50
S543	1956D	....	67,222,000	—	—	.40
a	1956D	bar/M (UNUM).............................	—	—	—	1.00
b	1956D	double MM & dome	—	—	.50	3.75
S544	1957	....	39,655,000	—	—	.50
S545	1957D	....	136,828,000	—	—	.30
a	1957D	MONTICELLO, two l, die br.............	—	—	—	1.00
b	1957D	double MM..................................	—	—	.75	3.75
c	1957D	double MM & profile.....................	—	—	.75	3.75
S546	1958	....	17,963,000	—	.20	1.00
a	1958	dot in front of date, 1958.............	—	—	.50	1.00
S547	1958D	....	168,249,000	—	—	.25
a	1958D	double MM..................................	—	—	.50	1.25
b	1958D	double MM & profile.....................	—	—	.50	1.75
c	1958D	bar/9-5, double MM......................	—	—	1.00	3.00
d	1958D	double U. S. AMERICA....................	—	—	.50	1.25
e	1958D	double bar 5...............................	—	—	.50	1.25

JEFFERSON NICKELS

Index #	Date	Description	Mintage	Good	Fine	Unc.
S548	1959	....	28,397,000	—	—	.50
a	1959	black beauty, dark alloy............................	—	—	—	1.00
b	1959	bar/5, double bar 5	—	—	1.00	2.50
c	1959	double dome................................	—	—	—	1.00
S549	1959D		160,738,000	—	—	.25
a	1959D	double MM................................	—	—	—	1.00
b	1959D	double curve, 9, imperfection..................	—	—	.50	1.25
c	1959D	double profile, MM, & dome..................	—	—	1.00	3.50
d	1959D	no balconies next to dome, filled die	—	—	1.75	5.50
S550	1960		57,107,000	—	—	.25
a	1960	double profile, & dome..........................	—	—	.50	1.25
b	1960	double LIBERTY, date & dome..............	—	—	1.00	2.50
c	1960	bars/E-zero..	—	—	.35	1.00
d	1960	bar/zero..	—	—	.35	1.00
e	1960	clog 6..	—	—	.25	1.00
f	1960	extended 6	—	—	.25	1.00
g	1960	rotated 345° (proof) $4.50	—	—	—	—
h	1960	triple dome, double design-lettering.........	—	—	—	8.50

BEWARE OF
1959
ALTERED
DATE
TO
1950

1959D
NORMAL

Index #	Date	Description	Mintage	Good	Fine	Unc.
S551	1960D		192,582,000	—	—	.25
a	1960D	double U. S. AMERICA,bar/E (LIBERTY).	—	—	.75	1.50
b	1960D	bar/R (LIBERTY)...............................	—	—	.50	1.25
c	1960D	bar/R & zero (date)...........................	—	—	.50	1.50
d	1960D	bar/ER..	—	—	.50	1.50
e	1960D	bar/BERT	—	—	.50	1.50
f	1960D	bar/BERT & zero	—	—	.50	1.50
g	1960D	bar/B, joined bottom 19.....................	—	—	.50	1.50
h	1960D	double MM..	—	—	.50	1.50
i	1960D	bar/E...	—	—	.35	1.00
j	1960D	bar/B...	—	—	.35	1.00
k	1960D	bar/zero, double MM..........................	—	—	.75	1.50
l	1960D	double date, MM & dome	—	—	1.00	3.00
m	1960D	double date, MM, dome, bar/BERTY & zero..	—	—	1.50	4.50
n	1960D	double building, MM, & MONTICELLO	—	—	1.00	2.50
o	1960D	double MM, bar/ER & 60......................	—	—	1.00	2.75
p	1960D	Stratus Cloud/dome............................	—	—	.50	1.75
q	1960D	14 diebreak errors	—	—	2.50	6.00
r	1960D	triple struck rev. double obv...................	—	—	200.00	—

TRIPLE STRUCK
1960D

Index #	Date	Description	Mintage	Good	Fine	Unc.

REENGRAVED
DATE AND LETTERING

DOUBLE DOME

1960 P
JEFFERSON
NICKEL

DOUBLE PROFILE

1960
BAR OVER O

1960 P
BARS
OVER E AND O

1960 P
EXTENDED
6

1960P
CLOGGED 6

Index #	Date	Description	Mintage	Good	Fine	Unc.
S552	1961	....	76,668,000	—	—	.25
a	1961	LIBERTY (middle bar of E missing)	proof $8.00			
b	1961	double date & dome	—	—	—	—
c	1961	(IIN) double I, "IN GOD WE TRUST"	—	—	1.00	2.00
d	1961	double 1 in date...................................	—	—	1.00	3.50
S553	1961D	....	229,342,000	—	—	.20
a	1961D	double MM..	—	—	.50	2.00
b	1961D	double date...	—	—	.50	2.00
c	1961D	double date, MM, profile & dome.............	—	—	1.00	3.00
d	1961D	bar/6	—	—	.50	1.00
e	1961D	bar/ET (LIBERTY)...................................	—	—	.50	1.00
f	1961D	bar/ERT...	—	—	.75	1.25
S554	1962	....	100,602,000	—	—	.25
a	1962	whiskered chin, bar/62..........................	—	—	.50	1.00
b	1962	double date...	—	—	.50	2.00
c	1962	bar/6	—	—	.50	1.00
d	1962	bar/2	—	—	.50	1.00
e	1962	double profile, date & dome....................	—	—	1.00	2.50
f	1962	double lettering rev. side........................	—	—	.50	1.00

JEFFERSON NICKELS

Index #	Date	Description	Mintage	Good	Fine	Unc.

1962 DOUBLE DATE

1962 BAR OVER 6 AND 2

Index #	Date	Description	Mintage	Good	Fine	Unc.
S555	1962D	....	280,195,000	—	—	.20
a	1962D	double date, MM & dome	—	—	.75	2.00
b	1962D	double MM..	—	—	.50	1.00
c	1962D	bar/62	—	—	.50	1.00
d	1962D	bar/2	—	—	.50	1.00
e	1962D	bar/6	—	—	.50	1.00
S556	1963	....	178,851,000	—	—	.20
a	1963	double date...	—	—	.50	1.00
b	1963	bar/3 & BERTY.......................................	—	—	.75	1.25
c	1963	E Pluribus unum (fill die)	—	—	—	1.00
d	1963	dot under R (liberty)................................	—	—	—	2.00
S557	1963D	....	276,829,000	—	—	.15
a	1963D	bar/6	—	—	.25	.75
b	1963D	bar/ERT..	—	—	.25	.75
c	1963D	bar/3	—	—	.25	.75
d	1963D	clash die	—	—	.25	.75
S558	1964	....	1,787,297,000	—	—	.15
a	1964	monocle eye, (die break).........................	—	—	—	.25
b	1964	large date, serf 4.....................................	—	—	—	.50
c	1964	small date, light serf 4............................	—	—	—	.50
d	1964	double MONTICELLO	—	—	—	1.00
e	1964	double date...	—	—	—	1.00
f	1964	double dome	—	—	—	.50
g	1964	frosted (proof)	—	—	—	2.75
h	1964	U.S. doubled	—	—	—	.75
i	1964	dot under 4...	—	—	—	2.00
S559	1964D	....	1,028,623,000	—	—	.15
a	1964D	monocle eye, (die break).........................	—	—	—	.25
b	1964D	double FIVE CENTS	—	—	—	.50
c	1964D	double "E PLURIBUS UNUM"...................	—	—	—	.50
d	1964D	double "MONTICELLO"	—	—	—	.50
e	1964D	double dome...	—	—	—	.50
f	1964D	double date...	—	—	—	.50
g	1964D	"E PL—UNUM" fill die	—	—	—	.50
h	1964D	double MM..	—	—	—	2.00

1964 LAMINATED PEEL

1964 D OFF CENTER

HALF DIMES 1794-1873

Index #	Date	Description	Mintage	Good	Fine	Unc.

1802
DRAPED BUST TYPE
(RARE)

OBVERSE

REVERSE

Index #	Date	Description	Mintage	Good	Fine	Unc.
S560	1794	....	—	150.00	475.00	1500.00
S561	1795	....	—	125.00	295.00	800.00
S562	1796	....	10,230	150.00	450.00	1000.00
a	1796	6/5 overdate....................	—	275.00	600.00	1500.00
b	1796	LIKERTY (fill die) "B".......	—	250.00	425.00	1200.00
S563	1797	15 stars...........................	44,527	125.00	310.00	950.00
a	1797	16 stars...........................	—	125.00	310.00	950.00
b	1797	13 stars...........................	—	150.00	350.00	975.00
S564	1800	....	24,000	125.00	300.00	900.00
a	1800	LIBEKTY (fill die) "R".......	—	125.00	300.00	900.00
S565	1801	....	33,910	125.00	300.00	900.00
S566	1802	rare	13,010	1200.00	2500.00	RARE
S567	1803	....	—	95.00	225.00	750.00
S568	1805	....	15,600	110.00	300.00	900.00

NO HALF DIMES KNOWN TO BE STRUCK DURING 1806-1828

Index #	Date	Description	Mintage	Good	Fine	Unc.
S569	1829	....	1,230,000	3.50	8.00	55.00
S570	1830	....	1,240,000	2.75	7.00	50.00
S571	1831	....	1,242,000	2.75	7.00	50.00
S572	1832	....	960,000	3.00	7.50	55.00
S573	1833	....	1,370,000	2.75	7.50	50.00
S574	1834	....	1,480,000	2.75	7.00	50.00
S575	1835	large date, lg. 5C.............	2,760,000	3.00	6.50	52.00
a	1835	large date, small 5C.........	—	3.00	6.50	52.00
b	1835	small date, large 5C.........	—	3.00	6.50	52.00
c	1835	small date, small 5C.........	—	3.00	6.50	52.00
S576	1836	large 5 C.........................	1,900,000	3.00	6.50	52.00
a	1836	small 5 C.........................	—	3.00	6.50	52.00
b	1836	double 5 in (5C) rev., double 3, and stars	—	4.50	9.50	85.00
S577	1837	large 5 C.........................	2,276,000	3.00	6.50	50.00
a	1837	small 5 C.........................	—	7.00	18.00	115.00
b	1837	small date, no stars..........	—	30.00	70.00	200.00
c	1837	large date, no stars..........	—	30.00	70.00	200.00
S578	18380	no stars...........................	—	55.00	115.00	475.00
S579	1838	large stars.......................	2,255,000	3.50	7.50	50.00
a	1838	small stars	—	4.50	8.50	53.00
S580	1839	....	1,069,000	3.75	6.00	40.00
S581	18390	....	1,096,000	5.50	9.75	55.00
S582	1840	....	1,344,000	3.75	6.00	42.00
S583	18400	drapery............................	935,000	5.50	11.00	85.00
a	18400	no drapery (left elbow)......	—	4.50	12.00	100.00
S584	1841	....	1,150,000	2.50	5.50	45.00
S585	18410	....	815,000	3.75	10.00	78.00
S586	1842	....	815,000	3.75	6.00	45.00
S587	18420	....	350,000	6.75	16.00	135.00
S588	1843	....	1,165,000	2.00	5.00	38.00
a	1843	triple cut date (proof)	rare	RARE		
S589	1844	....	430,000	3.00	8.50	50.00
a	1844	recut first 4 (proof)...........	rare	RARE		
b	1844	repunched 8.....................	—	4.50	12.00	55.00

HALF DIMES

Index #	Date	Description	Mintage	Good	Fine	Unc.
S590	18440		220,000	7.00	20.00	115.00
S591	1845		1,564,000	2.50	6.00	48.00
a	1845/3	overdate	—	17.00	48.00	300.00
S592	1846		27,000	55.00	90.00	300.00
S593	1847		1,274,000	2.50	6.00	35.00
S594	1848	large date	668,000	2.50	6.00	42.00
a	1848	medium date	—	2.50	6.50	42.00
b	1848	recut (48)	—	4.00	9.00	39.00
S595	18480		600,000	5.00	12.50	85.00
S596	1849		1,309,000	2.50	5.50	32.00
a	1849	recut 9	—	4.50	8.50	35.00
b	1849/6		—	3.50	11.00	40.00
c	1849/8		—	3.50	11.00	40.00
S597	18490		140,000	30.00	60.00	300.00
S598	1850		955,000	2.50	5.00	28.00
S599	18500		690,000	4.00	11.00	110.00
S600	1851		781,000	2.75	5.50	27.50
S601	18510		860,000	3.00	9.50	95.00
S602	1852		1,000,500	2.50	5.50	28.00
S603	18520		260,000	6.50	17.00	127.00
S604	1853	total mintage all types with arrows	13,345,000	3.50	7.50	40.00
a	1853	no arrows	—	9.00	25.00	85.00
b	1853	clash dies	—	—	—	—
S605	18530	with arrows, all types	2,360,000	3.50	7.00	50.00
a	18530	no arrows	—	65.00	135.00	500.00
S606	1854		5,740,000	2.50	4.00	30.00
a	1854	high date	—	2.75	6.50	32.00
S607	18540		1,560,000	2.50	5.00	38.00
S608	1855		1,750,000	2.50	4.00	30.00
S609	18550		600,000	4.00	8.25	95.00
S610	1856		4,880,000	1.75	3.00	28.00
S611	18560		1,100,000	2.00	5.00	40.00
a	18560	recut date	—	6.00	9.50	55.00
S612	1857		7,280,000	1.75	3.50	26.00
S613	18570		1,380,000	2.50	5.50	35.00
S614	1858		3,500,000	1.75	3.25	26.00
S615	18580		1,660,000	2.50	5.00	34.00
S616	1859		340,000	3.75	8.50	35.00
a	1859	obverse of 59, rev. of 60		PROOF $1800.00		
S617	18590		560,000	3.50	6.50	47.00
S618	1860		799,000	2.50	4.50	28.00
a	1860	obverse of 59, rcv. of 60	—	—	—	875.00
S619	18600		1,060,000	3.75	8.00	38.00
S620	1861		3,281,000	2.75	5.00	26.00
S621	1862		1,492,550	2.75	5.00	27.00
S622	1863		18,460	11.00	19.00	87.00
a	1863	recut date (18)	—	15.50	28.00	90.00
S623	1863S		100,000	11.00	20.00	90.00
S624	1864		470	PROOF $275.00		
S625	1864S		90,000	12.00	20.00	110.00
S626	1865		13,500	11.00	19.00	95.00
S627	1865S		120,000	9.00	14.00	90.00
a	1865S	overdate, 65/63	—	18.00	55.00	150.00
S628	1866		10,725	8.00	15.00	90.00
S629	1866S		120,000	6.00	14.00	80.00
S630	1867		8,625	8.50	20.00	96.00
S631	1867S		120,000	6.00	13.50	82.00
S632	1868		85,900	4.00	7.00	40.00
S633	1868S		280,000	3.50	6.50	47.50
S634	1869		208,000	3.50	6.00	40.00
S635	1869S		230,000	3.50	8.00	45.00
a	1869S	recut date	—	7.50	13.00	47.00

HALF DIMES

Index #	Date	Description	Mintage	Good	Fine	Unc.
S636	1870		536,000	2.50	5.50	30.00
S637	1871		1,488,000	2.50	5.50	28.00
S638	1871S		161,000	9.50	18.00	80.00
S639	1872		2,947,000	2.50	4.75	29.00
S640	1872S	all types, MM in wreath	837,000	2.75	7.50	32.00
a	1872S	MM under wreath	—	3.50	8.50	35.00
S641	1873		712,600	2.50	6.50	28.00
S642	1873S		324,000	2.75	7.00	35.00

DIMES 1796-1965

Index #	Date	Description	Mintage	Good	Fine	Unc.
S643	1796		22,135	275.00	675.00	2100.00
S644	1797	16 stars	—	225.00	550.00	1500.00
a	1797	13 stars	27,550	200.00	480.00	1350.00
S645	1798	all types	—	125.00	275.00	900.00
a	1798/97	13 stars	VERY RARE	—	—	—
b	1798/97	16 stars	—	150.00	300.00	950.00
c	1798	small 8	VERY RARE	—	—	—
d	1798	medium 8	—	115.00	290.00	800.00
S646	1800		21,760	100.00	185.00	725.00
S647	1801		34,640	110.00	275.00	785.00
a	1801	(R) in LIBERTY recut	—	110.00	275.00	725.00
S648	1802		10,975	130.00	300.00	840.00
S649	1803		33,040	115.00	265.00	800.00
S650	1804	13 stars, all types	8,265	130.00	285.00	1300.00
a	1804	14 stars	—	130.00	285.00	1300.00
S651	1805		120,780	65.00	115.00	600.00
S652	1807		165,000	60.00	110.00	450.00
S653	1809		44,710	40.00	85.00	270.00
S654	1811/9	overdate	65,180	28.00	55.00	175.00
S655	1814	large date, all types	421,500	10.00	21.00	190.00
a	1814	small date	—	12.00	20.00	180.00
S656	1820	large zero, all types	942,587	7.00	15.00	200.00
a	1820	small zero	—	6.00	14.50	85.00
S657	1821	large date, all types	1,186,500	8.50	18.00	130.00
a	1821	small date	—	8.50	18.00	130.00
S658	1822		100,000	48.50	124.00	640.00
S659	1823/22	overdate, small E's	440,000	11.00	22.00	150.00
a	1823/22	overdate, large E's	—	11.00	22.00	150.00
S660	1824/22	overdate	—	12.00	30.00	180.00
S661	1825		510,000	10.00	21.00	150.00
S662	1828	small date, all types	125,000	14.00	25.00	185.00
a	1828	large date	—	22.50	50.00	210.00
S663	1829	small date, all types	770,000	6.50	12.00	135.00
a	1829	medium date	—	6.00	12.00	135.00
b	1829	large date	—	9.50	25.00	135.00
S664	1830	small date, all types	510,000	5.00	9.50	125.00
a	1830	large date	—	5.00	9.50	125.00
S665	1831		771,350	4.00	9.50	125.00
S666	1832		522,500	4.00	9.50	125.00
S667	1833		485,000	4.50	9.50	125.00
S668X	1834	small 4, all types	635,000	4.50	9.50	125.00
a	1834	large 4	—	4.50	9.50	125.00
S668	1835					
S669	1836		1,410,000	4.50	9.25	125.00
S670	1837	draped bust type, all types	1,190,000	4.50	9.00	125.00
a	1837	liberty seated type, no stars, small date	1,042,000	4.75	9.00	125.00
			—	38.00	90.00	240.00
b	1837	liberty seated type, no stars, large date	—	38.00	90.00	240.00

66

DIMES

Index #	Date	Description	Mintage	Good	Fine	Unc.
S671	18380	liberty seated type, no stars, ...	402,434	55.00	120.00	525.00
S672	1838	liberty seated, with stars, sm. date, all types	1,992,500	12.00	28.00	85.00
a	1838	liberty seated, with stars, large date	—	5.75	9.50	70.00
S673	1839	....	1,053,000	4.00	8.00	45.00
S674	18390	....	1,243,000	4.50	11.00	55.00
S675	1840	....	1,358,000	4.00	10.00	40.00
S676	18400	....	1,175,000	5.00	14.00	45.00
S677	1841	....	1,622,500	2.75	5.50	38.00
S678	18410	....	2,007,500	2.75	6.50	60.00
S679	1842	....	1,887,500	3.50	6.00	40.00
S680	18420	....	2,020,000	3.75	9.00	58.00
S681	1843	....	1,370,000	3.00	5.50	39.00
a	1843	recut date	—	4.50	14.00	50.00
S682	18430	....	150,000	16.00	32.00	240.00
S683	1844	....	72,500	22.00	65.00	265.00
S684	1845	....	1,755,000	2.50	6.50	35.00
S685	18450	....	230,000	8.50	14.00	85.00
S686	1846	....	31,300	15.00	30.00	170.00
S687	1847	....	245,000	5.50	10.00	55.00
S688	1848	....	451,000	4.50	7.00	45.00
S689	1849	....	839,000	2.75	5.00	40.00
S690	18490	....	300,000	7.00	14.00	120.00
S691	1850	....	1,931,500	2.75	6.00	35.00
S692	18500	....	510,000	5.50	14.00	65.00
S693	1851	....	1,026,000	2.75	6.00	30.00
S694	18510	....	400,000	6.00	11.00	65.00
S695	1852	....	1,535,500	2.75	5.50	30.00
S696	18520	....	430,000	6.50	13.00	80.00
S697	1853	no arrows	95,000	16.00	27.00	115.00
a	1853	with arrows	12,173,000	3.00	6.00	31.00
S698	18530	....	1,100,000	4.00	10.00	46.00
S699	1854	....	4,470,000	3.00	5.75	32.00
S700	18540	....	1,770,000	3.00	5.75	35.00
S701	1855	....	2,075,000	3.00	5.75	35.00
S702	1856	....	5,780,000	2.75	5.50	28.00
a	1856	large date, ...	—	3.00	7.50	42.00
S703	18560	....	1,180,000	3.00	6.50	42.00
a	18560	recut date	—	4.50	8.50	48.00
b	18560	repunched 56, odd shaped 8, dot pointed stars, 10 o'clock		8.00	24.00	85.00
S704	1856S	....	70,000	28.00	67.00	295.00
S705	1857	....	5,580,000	2.75	5.50	30.00
S706	18570	....	1,540,000	2.75	5.50	35.00
S707	1858	....	1,540,000	2.00	4.75	30.00
S708	18580	....	290,000	5.00	8.00	52.00
S709	1858S	....	60,000	16.00	45.00	250.00
S710	1859	....	430,000	2.75	5.75	33.00
a	1859	no arrows, rev. of 1860 (pattern)	—		$3,000.00	
S711	18590	....	480,000	2.75	5.75	50.00
S712	1859S	....	—	19.00	40.00	160.00
S713	1860S	....	140,000	9.50	25.00	115.00
S742	1873	close 3, all types	1,568,600	2.75	6.50	29.00
a	1873	open 3	—	3.50	11.00	37.00
b	1873	arrows	2,378,000	10.00	30.00	110.00
S743	1873CC	(Unique) no arrows	12,400	—	—	—
a	1873CC	arrows	18,791	280.00	480.00	1500.00
S781	1892	....	12,121,000	.50	2.75	18.00
S782	18920	....	3,841,700	2.00	5.00	35.00
S783	1892S	....	990,710	16.00	29.00	105.00

Index #	Date	Description	Mintage	Good	Fine	Unc.

RARE
1894-S DIME

BARBER OR LIBERTY DIMES 1892-1916

Index #	Date	Description	Mintage	Good	Fine	Unc.
S784	1893		3,340,000	1.50	4.00	20.00
a	1893/2	overdate, rare	—	—	—	—
S786	1893S		2,491,000	4.00	11.00	53.00
a	1893S	double MM	—	6.50	16.00	70.00
S790	1895S	double MM	1,120,000	15.00	35.00	140.00
S802	1899		19,580,000	.40	1.80	18.00
a	1899	recut date	—	—	8.50	30.00
S803	18990		2,650,000	3.00	8.50	95.00
S804	1899S		1,867,000	3.00	8.50	63.00
S805	1900		17,600,000	.25	1.75	16.00
S806	19000		2,010,000	2.75	9.00	95.00
S807	1900S		5,168,000	2.00	6.00	48.00
S808	1901		18,860,000	.25	1.75	16.00
S809	1901S		593,022	20.00	86.00	480.00
S810	19010		5,620,000	1.30	7.00	95.00
a	19010	double MM	—	2.00	8.75	95.00
S811	1902		21,380,000	.25	1.50	16.00
S812	19020		4,500,000	1.00	5.50	65.00
S813	1902S		2,070,000	3.00	9.00	85.00
S814	1903		19,500,000	.25	1.50	18.00
S815	19030		8,180,000	.75	5.25	49.00
S816	1903S		613,000	8.00	16.00	160.00
S817	1904		14,601,000	.25	1.25	18.00
S818	1904S		800,000	8.00	17.00	120.00
S819	1905		14,552,000	.25	1.00	18.00

19050
MICRO O
LARGE O

Index #	Date	Description	Mintage	Good	Fine	Unc.
S820	19050	large MM, all types	3,400,000	1.50	4.50	60.00
a	19050	micro. MM	—	2.75	7.00	70.00
S828	19070	recut U.S.A.	—	1.00	4.00	26.00
S850	1914D		11,908,000	.30	1.75	22.00
a	1914D	double MM shift west	—	.75	3.50	30.00
b	1914D	double MM shift east	—	.75	3.50	30.00

MERCURY DIMES 1916-1945

Index #	Date	Description	Mintage	Good	Fine	Unc.
S856	1916		22,180,000	.25	1.75	9.00
a	1916	micro. double date	—	1.00	4.00	12.00
b	1916	ONF, fill die ONE rev.	—	—	5.00	14.00
S857	1916D		264,000	85.00	190.00	700.00
S858	1916S		10,450,000	.85	3.75	17.00
a	1916S	micro. double date and LIBERTY	—	2.50	8.00	26.00
b	1916S	double MM	—	2.50	8.00	25.00
S859	1917		55,230,000	.25	1.75	10.50
a	1917	micro. double date	—	1.00	2.50	13.50
S860	1917D		9,402,000	1.25	6.00	65.00
S861	1917S		27,330,000	1.00	3.00	24.00

DIMES

Index #	Date	Description	Mintage	Good	Fine	Unc.
S862	1918		26,680,000	.25	1.50	26.00
a	1918	long first 1, die break	—	1.00	4.00	30.00
S863	1918D		22,674,000	.50	3.50	40.00
a	1918D	double date	—	1.50	5.50	55.00
S864	1918S		19,300,000	.50	2.75	32.00
a	1918S	micro. double date & LIBERTY	—	1.50	4.75	45.00
S865	1919		35,740,000	.25	1.75	30.00
a	1919	micro double date & part dble. LIBERTY .	—	1.25	2.75	35.00
S866	1919D		9,939,000	1.00	7.00	95.00
a	1919D	micro. double date	—	1.50	8.50	100.00
S867	1919S		8,850,000	1.50	6.50	105.00
a	1919S	micro double date	—	1.50	8.00	115.00
S868	1920		50,030,000	.25	1.00	13.00
a	1920	micro. double date & LIBERTY	—	1.25	5.75	16.50
S869	1920D		19,171,000	.75	4.50	36.00
a	1920D	micro. double date & MM	—	1.50	5.75	40.00
b	1920D	heavy die break over 1, also clash dies	—		8.00	65.00
S870	1920S		13,820,000	.50	3.00	36.00
S871	1921		1,230,000	10.00	45.00	305.00
a	1921	micro. double date	—	11.50	49.00	310.00
S872	1921D		1,080,000	12.50	55.00	290.00

**1921 P
DOUBLE
DATE**

**1923 P
FILLED
DIE**

Index #	Date	Description	Mintage	Good	Fine	Unc.
S873	1923		50,130,000	.25	1.25	16.00
a	1923	micro. double date	—	1.00	2.50	18.50
b	1923	partial date 192 —, filled die	—	.50	1.75	19.00
c	1923	double LIBERTY	—	.50	1.75	19.00
	*1923D	several known to exist, a con-troversial piece considered a product of foreign origin	—	—	—	—
S874	1923S		6,440,000	1.25	5.00	95.00
a	1923S	micro. double date	—	1.50	6.50	100.00
S875	1924		24,010,000	.25	1.00	17.00
a	1924	micro. double date	—	1.00	3.50	18.95
S876	1924D		6,810,000	1.50	4.75	60.00
a	1924D	micro. double date & LIBERTY	—	1.75	8.00	75.00
S877	1824S		7,120,000	1.00	4.50	70.00
a	1924S	micro. double date	—	1.50	5.50	75.00
b	1924S	clash dies	—		7.50	75.00
S878	1925		25,610,000	.25	1.25	17.00
a	1925	micro. double date	—	.75	1.50	18.50
S879	1925D		5,117,000	1.00	7.50	310.00
a	1925D	micro double date, LIBERTY	—	1.50	9.00	310.00
S880	1925S		5,850,000	1.00	4.75	95.00
S881	1926		32,160,000	.25	1.00	14.00
S882	1926D		6,828,000	.50	1.75	55.00
a	1926D	micro. double date	—	1.00	4.75	60.00
S883	1926S		1,520,000	4.00	14.00	160.00
S884	1927		28,080,000	.25	.75	12.00
a	1927	micro double date	—	.50	1.75	15.00
S885	1927D		4,812,000	1.00	4.75	225.00
a	1927D	micro double date & LIBERTY	—	2.00	6.75	235.00
S886	1927S		4,770,000	1.00	4.50	95.00
S887	1928		19,480,000	.15	.75	12.00
a	1928	micro. double date	—	.75	1.75	15.00

69

DIMES

Index #	Date	Description	Mintage	Good	Fine	Unc.
S888	1928D	....	4,161,000	.50	3.75	95.00
a	1928D	micro. double date............................	—	1.50	5.75	100.00
S889	1928S	....	7,400,000	.50	3.75	65.00

1924 D DOUBLE DATE

1936 P MICRO DOUBLE DATE

Index #	Date	Description	Mintage	Good	Fine	Unc.
S890	1928S	double MM...............................	—	2.00	7.50	80.00
a	1929	micro. double date........................	—	.50	1.25	9.75
S891	1929D		5,034,000	.50	1.75	14.00
a	1929D	micro. double date & MM	—	1.50	4.75	18.00
S892	1929S		4,730,000	.50	1.75	19.00
a	1929S	double MM................................	—	.75	3.75	21.00
S893	1930		6,770,000	.25	1.00	13.50
a	1930	micro. double date & LIBERTY............	—	1.00	2.50	15.50
S894	1930S		1,843,000	1.00	4.50	48.00
a	1930S	micro. double date & LIBERTY............	—	1.50	6.00	55.00
S895	1931		3,150,000	.50	2.50	21.00
S896	1931D		1,260,000	3.50	8.50	55.00
S897	1931S		1,800,000	2.50	6.50	48.00
S898	1934		24,080,000	.15	.45	8.00
S899	1934D		6,772,000	.40	1.75	12.50
a	1934D	large D/ small D, MM	—	1.00	5.50	18.00
b	1934D	double date & MM	—	1.00	5.50	18.00
S900	1935		58,830,000	.15	.75	6.00
a	1935	double LIBERTY	—	.50	1.50	7.00
b	1935	double date................................	—	.50	1.50	7.00
S901	1935D		10,477,000	.20	1.00	22.00

1929 S DOUBLE S

1934 D MICRO DOUBLE DATE

Index #	Date	Description	Mintage	Good	Fine	Unc.
a	1935D	micro. double date & LIBERTY................	—	1.00	2.50	25.00
S902	1935S		15,840,000	.25	.75	8.50
S903	1936		87,504,000	—	.25	2.50
a	1936	micro. double date............................	—	.50	1.00	4.00
S904	1936D		16,132,000	—	.25	17.00
a	1936D	micro. double date & MM	—	.75	1.75	24.00
S905	1936S		9,210,000	—	.50	9.50
S906	1937		56,865,000	—	—	2.75
S907	1937D		14,146,000	—	.25	5.75
S908	1937S		9,740,000	—	.25	7.00
a	1937S	micro. double date & MM	—	.50	1.50	9.00
S909	1938		22,198,000	—	—	2.75
S910	1938D		5,537,000	—	.50	6.75
S911	1938S		8,090,000	—	.50	6.75
a	1938S	micro. double date & MM	—	.50	1.50	9.50
S912	1939		67,749,000	—	—	2.00
S913	1939D		24,394,000	—	—	3.50
S914	1939S		10,540,000	—	.50	6.00
S915	1940		65,361,000	—	—	1.75
a	1940	micro. double date............................	—	.50	1.25	2.75
S916	1940D		21,198,000	—	—	1.75

DIMES

Index #	Date	Description	Mintage	Good	Fine	Unc.
S917	1940S		21,560,000	—	—	2.50
a	1940S	small MM	—	—	.50	3.00
b	1940S	micro. double date	—	.50	1.00	4.75
c	1940S	double MM	—	1.00	3.00	7.00
d	1940S	missing bridge nose (filled die)	—	—	—	2.50
S918	1941		175,106,000	—	—	1.00
a	1941	19.41, dot die break	—	—	.75	2.75
S920	1941D		45,634,000	—	—	2.00
a	1941D	micro. double date	—	—	1.00	3.50
S921	1941S		43,090,000	—	—	2.50
a	1941S	small MM, SERIF, S	—	—	1.50	3.75
b	1941S	micro. double date	—	—	1.00	2.50
c	1941S	double MM	—	1.00	2.75	5.50
d	1941S	S/horizontal S	—	—	—	—
e	1941S	Large Knob, MM	—	—	.50	2.50
S922	1942		205,432,000	—	—	1.00
a	1942/1	overdate	—	65.00	95.00	410.00
b	1942/41		—	65.00	100.00	425.00
c	1942	micro. double date	—	—	1.00	2.50
d	1942	die break through 42	—	—	1.00	1.75
e	1942	clash dies base of hair to neck, right of 4	—	—	—	2.50
S923	1942D		60,740,000	—	—	1.50
a	1942D	/41, partial 1, shows upper and lower parts of 1 in front of 2, the 4 shows double lower bar similar to 42 but in opposite direction. A much over-looked and underrated variety.	—	17.00	40.00	115.00
b	1942D	micro. double date	—	—	.75	2.00
S924	1942S		49,300,000	—	—	2.50
a	1942S	micro. double date & LIBERTY	—	—	1.50	3.75
b	1942S	double MM	—	—	3.75	6.50
S925	1943		191,710,000	—	—	1.00

1942 P
42 OVER 1

1942 MERCURY DIME
(METAL RUN OUT)

a	1943	micro. double date	—	.50	1.50	3.75
S926	1943D		71,949,000	—	—	1.50
a	1943D	double MM	—	—	2.50	3.75
S927	1943S		60,000,000	—	—	1.75
a	1943S	double MM	—	—	2.75	5.00
b	1943S	micro. double date & LIBERTY	—	—	3.50	5.75
S928	1944		231,410,000	—	—	1.00
a	1944	micro. double date & LIBERTY	—	—	2.75	4.50
S929	1944D		62,224,000	—	—	1.00
a	1944D	micro. double date & LIBERTY	—	—	2.75	4.50
S930	1944S		49,490,000	—	—	1.10
a	1944S	micro. double date & LIBERTY	—	—	2.75	4.50
S931	1945		159,130,000	—	—	1.00
a	1945	micro. double date & LIBERTY	—	—	2.50	4.50
S932	1945D		40,245,000	—	—	1.10
a	1945D	micro. double date & LIBERTY	—	—	2.50	4.50

DIMES

MICRO S   **LARGE S**

Index #	Date	Description	Mintage	Good	Fine	Unc.
S933	1945S		41,920,000	—	—	1.00
a	1945S	micro. double date & LIBERTY	—	—	2.50	4.50
b	1945S	micro MM	—	—	1.50	17.00
c	1945S	micro. double MM	—	—	2.00	24.00

**1945 P
MICRO DOUBLE
DATE & LIBERTY**

**1943 P
ENGRAVERS
INITIAL**

ROOSEVELT DIMES 1946-1966

Index #	Date	Description	Mintage	Good	Fine	Unc.
S934	1946		255,250,000	—	—	1.00
S935	1946D		61,043,000	—	—	1.50
S936	1946S		27,900,000	—	—	2.25
a	1946S	micro. double date	—	—	2.00	3.00
S944	1949D		26,034,000	—	—	3.75
a	1949D	micro. double date	—	—	1.50	4.75
b	1949D	double MM	—	—	1.50	4.75
S947	1950D		46,803,000	—	—	2.50
a	1950D	STATE $ die break through S	—	—	2.50	15.00
S951	1951S		31,630,000	—	—	12.00
a	1951S	large & small 1 in date, blaze across rev..	—	—	1.50	15.00
S952	1952		99,122,000	—	—	1.00
a	1952	horned head	—	—	.75	2.00
S954	1952S		44,419,000	—	—	4.75
a	1952S	double MM	—	—	1.00	5.75

**THE HITLER MUSTACHE (DIEBREAK)
ROOSEVELT DIME**

ROOSEVELT GOATEE CHIN TYPE

Index #	Date	Description	Mintage	Good	Fine	Unc.
S955	1953P	Hitler Mustache	—	.75	3.50	15.00
S956	1953D		136,433,000	—	—	1.00
a	1953D	double MM	—	—	.75	2.00
S959	1954D		106,397,000	—	—	.75
a	1954D	double MM	—	—	.75	2.50

DIMES

Index #	Date	Description	Mintage	Good	Fine	Unc.
S960	1954S		22,860,000	—	—	1.50
a	1954S	double MM	—	—	.75	3.00
S961	1955		12,828,000	—	.75	3.50
a	1955	horned head, die break	—	—	1.00	4.00
S962	1955D		13,959,000	—	.50	3.25
a	1955D	double MM	—	—	1.00	4.00
S965	1956D		108,015,100	—	—	.50
a	1956D	SFATES (first T appears as F) a die break or clash die	—	—	2.50	5.50
S966	1957		161,407,000	—	—	.50
a	1957	die break through date	—	—	—	.75
S967	1957D		113,354,000	—	—	.40
a	1957D	wart on nose, die break	—	—	—	1.00
b	195/D	small 7/ large 7	—	—	2.00	5.50
c	1957D	small 7	—	—	2.00	6.00

1962 D ROOSEVELT DIME WITH DOT OVER "R"

ROOSEVELT DIME WITH WART ON EYEBROW

Index #	Date	Description	Mintage	Good	Fine	Unc.
d	1957D	wart on eyebrow	—	.25	1.00	2.50
S969	1958D		136,564,000	—	—	.25
a	1958D	wart on nose, die break	—	—	—	1.00
b	1958D	double MM	—	—	—	1.50
S971	1959D		164,919,000	—	—	.25
a	1959D	double MM	—	—	—	1.00
S972	1960		72,081,000	—	—	.25
a	1960	die br. diagonally through E of WE	—	—	—	.50
b	1960	die br. diagonally rim to bottom of E	—	—	—	.50
S973	1960D		200,160,000	—	—	.25
a	1960D	double MM	—	—	—	.75
S975	1961D		209,146,000	—	—	.20
a	1961D	double MM	—	—	—	.75
S976	1962		75,668,000	—	—	.20
a	1962	goatee chin	—	—	—	2.00
b	1962	diagonal die br. through O of ONE	—	—	—	.75
S977	1962D		334,948,000	—	—	.20
a	1962D	dot, in god	—	—	.75	2.00
S979	1963D		421,476,000	—	—	.20
a	1963D	double MM	—	—	—	.75
a	1963D	double 1, and IN GOD WE TRUST	—	—	.75	2.00

SERIF ON 1 AND POINTED 9

STRAIGHT 1 BLUNT 9

| | 1964P-D | Pointed and Blunt Tail 9 Variety | — | — | — | — |

DIMES

Index #	Date	Description	Mintage	Good	Fine	Unc.
S980	1964		—	—	—	.20
a	1964	blunt tail 9	—	—	—	.20
b	1964	pointed tail 9 our est. less than	2,000,000	—	—	1.00
c	1964	double point W, in WE (Dot)	—	—	—	.35
d	1964	filled die, WE	—	—	—	.35
e	1964	proof pointed tail 9 in proof set less than	5,000	Proof	Set	16.00
f	1964	proof blunt tail 9 in proof set	—	Proof	Set	12.00
g	1964	proof set, pointed tail 9 dime, RHL cent	—	Proof	Set	17.00
h	1964	proof set, blunt tail 9 dime, PHL cent	—	Proof	Set	12.00
i	1964	proof set, pointed tail 9 dime, PHL cent	—	Proof	Set	12.00
j	1964	proof set, vanishing tail 9 dime, RHL cent (Pointed)		Rare Proof Set		18.00
k	1964	proof set, vanishing tail 9 dime, PHL cent (Pointed)	—	—	—	17.50
l	1964	micro double date proof set dime	—	—	—	60.00
m	1964	wart on eyebrow	—	—	—	.75
n	1964	thick dime (38.5) gr.	—	—	—	8.00
o	1964	Joined (AM) AMERICA (Large)	—	—	—	.20
p	1964	Spaced (AM) AMERICA (Small)	—	—	—	1.00

1964 JOINED (AM) AMERICA (Large)

1964 SPACED (AM) AMERICA (Small)

Index #	Date	Description	Mintage	Good	Fine	Unc.
S981	1964D		—	—	—	.20
a	1964D	pointed tail 9 our est. less than	40,000,000	—	—	.50
b	1964D	blunt tail 9	—	—	—	.20
c	1964D	joined 19, diagonal die br.	—	—	—	.50
d	1964D	filled die 4	—	—	—	.50
e	1964D	micro. double MM & LIBERTY	—	—	—	1.00
f	1964D	double MM, bar LI-BERTY, spiked chin	—	—	—	1.25
g	1964D	Joined (AM) AMERICA (Large)	—	—	—	.20
h	1964D	Spaced (AM) AMERICA (Small)	—	—	—	1.00

The clad coin series started with the year 1965. The composition of the contents are as follows; 1965 dime has 75% copper alloyed with 25% nickel bonded on a core of pure copper.

Index #	Date	Description	Mintage	Good	Fine	Unc.
S981-5	1965		—	—	—	.15
a	1965	missing dot (us unum) rev	—	—	—	.75
b	1965	bandaid on nose	—	—	—	.75
c	1965	missing bridge nose	—	—	—	.75
d	1965	dot over 6	—	—	—	2.00

TWENTY CENT PIECES 1875-1878

Index #	Date	Description	Mintage	Good	Fine	Unc.
S984	1875S	....	1,155,000	12.50	26.00	90.00
a	1875S	double MM..................................	—	14.00	32.00	100.00
b	1875S	double MM, circular die break Rev.	—	14.00	32.00	100.00
S986	1876CC	....	10,000			8,500.00

**1876 CC
DOUBLE LIBERTY
AND STARS**

a	1876CC	double LIBERTY in shield & stars.................................	—	—		9,000.00

QUARTERS 1796-TO DATE

**DRAPED BUST
TYPE**

OBVERSE

**REVERSE
SMALL EAGLE**

OBVERSE

**REVERSE
HERALDIC
EAGLE**

BUST TYPE

Index #	Date	Description	Mintage	Good	Fine	Unc.
S992	1806	....	206,124	45.00	100.00	650.00
a	1806/5	overdate..................................	—	55.00	120.00	700.00
S995	1818	....	361,174	17.00	44.00	225.00
a	1818/15	....	—	18.00	47.00	350.00
S996	1819	large 9..................................	144,000	17.00	39.00	210.00
a	1819	small 9..................................	—	17.00	39.00	210.00
S997	1820	large zero.............................	127,000	15.00	33.00	165.00
a	1820	small zero.............................	—	15.00	33.00	165.00
S999	1822	....	64,000	18.00	45.00	250.00
a	1822	25 over 50 c(rev. side)...........	—	150.00	300.00	1400.00
S1000	1823/22	....	17,800	500.00	1050.00	2000.00
S1002	1825/22	all types..................................	168,000	19.00	36.00	200.00
a	1825/23	....	—	19.00	36.00	200.00
b	1825/24	....	—	19.00	36.00	200.00

QUARTERS

Index #	Date	Description	Mintage	Good	Fine	Unc.
S1003	1827	curl base 2 in (25c)	rare	—	—	—
a	1827	square base 2 in (25c)	rare	—	—	—
S1004	1828		102,000	17.00	35.00	195.00
a	1828	25/50c, rev. side	—	50.00	85.00	475.00
S1005	1831	small letters	398,000	8.00	18.00	95.00
a	1831	large letters	—	8.00	18.00	95.00
b	1831	a large letter, large over small date	rare	—	—	—
S1015	18400	no drapery, at elbow	425,200	6.00	15.00	75.00
a	18400	drapery	—	6.00	15.00	75.00
S1018	1842	small date Proofs only	rare	—	—	—
a	1842	large date	—	7.00	16.00	60.00
S1019	18420	small date	769,000	15.00	26.00	95.00
a	18420	large date	—	6.50	15.00	70.00
S1026	1847		734,000	5.00	11.00	45.00
a	1847/47		—	10.00	28.00	75.00
S1037	1853		15,254,000	4.00	10.00	55.00
a	1853/52	no arrows, no rays	—	60.00	110.00	420.00
S1046	1856S		286,000	4.50	7.00	25.00
a	1856S	large/ small S, MM	—	25.00	50.00	180.00
S1084	1873	closed 3, no arrows	220,000	9.00	18.00	49.00
a	1873	open 3, no arrows	—	8.00	16.00	45.00
b	1873	arrows	1,263,700	21.00	35.00	125.00
S1085	1873CC	no arrows	4,000	500.00	800.00	—
a	1873CC	arrows	12,462	350.00	675.00	—

1877 S OVER HORIZONTAL S ENLARGED VIEW

Index #	Date	Description	Mintage	Good	Fine	Unc.
S1096	1876CC		4,944,000	3.50	6.50	35.00
a	1876CC	recut 6	—	4.50	9.50	45.00
S1097	1877S		8,996,000	4.50	8.00	30.00
a	1877S	double MM, S/ horizontal S	—	27.00	100.00	200.00

BARBER HEAD TYPE QUARTER 1892-1916

Index #	Date	Description	Mintage	Good	Fine	Unc.
S1117	1892		8,237,000	.50	3.75	22.00
a	1892	type 1, wing covers half of E of UNITED	—	—	4.50	25.00
b	1892	type 2, wing covers most of E of UNITED	—	—	—	—
S1135	1898		11,100,000	.50	3.75	21.00
a	1898/98		—	4.75	9.75	35.00
S1190	1916D		6,540,000	.50	3.75	25.00
a	1916D	double MM	—	1.00	6.50	30.00

STANDING LIBERTY QUARTERS 1916-1930

There are two types of reverses of the 1917 issue. Type 1 has no stars under the eagle, type 2 has 3 stars under the eagle.

The 1916 quarter has the reverse of type 1, no stars under the eagle a worn off date of 1916 and 1917 type 1 can be difficult to distinguish from each other. To help identify them the following illustrations shows 3 different type cloak folds at the left of the foot above the date.

QUARTERS

Index #	Date	Description	Mintage	Good	Fine	Unc.

	1916					
	SQUARE FOLD CLOAK	1917 TYPE 1 OVAL FOLD CLOAK		1917 TYPE 2 DIAGONAL FOLD CLOAK		

Index #	Date	Description	Mintage	Good	Fine	Unc.
S1191	1916		52,000	240.00	475.00	1100.00
S1192	1917	type 1 no stars under eagle	8,792,000	1.00	6.50	45.00
S1193	1917	type 2 stars under eagle	13,880,000	1.50	8.50	49.00

The Standing Liberty quarter series has a good many varieties of "Clashed Die" impressions. They are identified as follows; letters of "E PLURIBUS" and eagles wing folds transposed to the obverse, near knee and cloak. Impression are also known near Legend and eagles wings.

S1195	1917D	type 2	6,244,000	6.50	19.00	70.00
a	1917D	type 2 Clash die "E" and wing folds near knee	—	8.00	25.00	80.00
S1196	1917S	typo 1	1,952,000	7.00	19.00	65.00
a	1917S	type 1 Clash die "E" and wing folds near knee	—	9.00	28.00	85.00
S1200	1918S		11,072,000	4.50	10.00	60.00

1918 S
8 OVER 7

1926 S
DIEBREAK
ON WING OR
CLASH
DIE

a	1918S	clash die "E" and wing folds near knee	—	5.00	12.00	75.00
b	1918S	/7 overdate	rare	225.00	575.00	3500.00
S1206	1920S		6,380,000	4.50	17.00	65.00
a	1920S	extra fold in cloak	—	5.50	18.00	70.00
S1207	1921		1,916,000	25.00	57.00	200.00
a	1921	clash dies	—	28.00	60.00	215.00
S1208	1923		9,716,000	1.00	6.00	24.00
a	1923	clash dies	—	1.50	7.50	30.00
S1212	1924S		2,860,000	10.00	19.00	48.00
a	1924S	clash dies	—	11.00	21.00	50.00
S1214	1926		11,316,000	.75	4.00	24.00
a	1926	clash dies	—	1.00	5.00	29.00
S1216	1926S		2,700,000	2.00	12.50	140.00
a	1926S	clash dies, many impressions	—	2.75	15.00	150.00
b	1926S	extra fold in cloak, scarce	—	3.00	16.00	160.00

1926 S
DIEBREAK
IN FOLD

WITHOUT
DIEBREAK

QUARTERS

Index #	Date	Description	Mintage	Good	Fine	Unc.
c	1926S	extra fold, 6/0	—	4.50	18.00	165.00
d	1926S	6/0	—	2.75	11.00	144.00
S1220	1928		6,336,000	.50	2.75	22.00
a	1928	clash dies	—	1.00	3.75	25.00
S1221	1928D		1,627,000	1.00	4.50	28.00
a	1928D	clash dies	—	1.50	6.00	32.00
S1222	1928S		2,644,000	1.00	3.75	21.00
a	1928S	clash dies	—	1.75	5.25	27.00
S1223	1929		11,140,000	.50	2.75	18.00
a	1929	clash dies	—	1.00	3.75	22.00
S1225	1929S		1,764,000	1.50	4.50	25.00
a	1929S	clash dies	—	1.75	5.50	29.00
S1226	1930		5,632,000	.50	2.75	18.00
a	1930	clash dies	—	1.00	3.75	22.00

WASHINGTON QUARTERS 1932-1966

**1934
WASHINGTON
QUARTER**

Index #	Date	Description	Mintage	Good	Fine	Unc.
S1229	1932D		436,800	16.00	35.00	185.00
a	1932D	double MM	—	17.00	37.00	190.00
S1230	1932S		408,000	16.00	35.00	110.00
a	1932S	double MM	—	17.00	37.00	115.00
S1231	1934		31,912,000	—	1.50	16.00
a	1934	type 1, light motto	—	1.00	4.50	19.00
b	1934	type 2, medium letters in motto, middle stroke of "W" low	—	.50	1.50	17.00

1934 P
DOUBLE
DATE

1934 P
NORMAL

1934
DOUBLE
MOTTO

1934
NORMAL

Index #	Date	Description	Mintage	Good	Fine	Unc.
c	1934	type 3, middle stroke in "W" high	—	.75	3.00	26.00
d	1934	type 4, double shift "motto" date & lettering same as the 1955 double die shift cent, but rarer	—	30.00	110.00	500.00
S1238	1936D		5,374,000	1.00	8.00	225.00
a	1936D	double MM	—	1.50	10.00	250.00
S1256	1942S		19,384,000	—	1.00	15.00
a	1942S	double MM	—	.50	2.00	18.00
b	1942S	double profile & MM	—	1.00	3.00	20.00

QUARTERS

Index #	Date	Description	Mintage	Good	Fine	Unc.
S1259	1943S	....	21,700,000	—	—	5.75
a	1943S	double MM....................................	—	1.00	3.00	11.00
b	1943S	double die shift.............................	—	—	9.00	55.00
S1265	1945S	....	17,004,000	—	—	2.75
a	1945S	large MM.......................................	—	—	—	3.00
b	1945S	small MM	—	—	—	3.00
c	1945S	double MM, liberty & motto	—	1.25	4.50	8.00
S1272	1948	....	35,196,000	—	—	2.00
a	1948	out of level die, double LIBERTY & hairline	—	.50	2.00	6.00
S1279	1950S	....	10,284,000	—	—	5.00
a	1950S	double MM....................................	—	1.00	3.50	7.00
S1282	1951S	....	8,948,000	—	—	6.75
a	1951S	double MM....................................	—	1.00	3.50	9.00
S1284	1952D	....	49,795,000	—	—	2.50
a	1952D	double MM....................................	—	.75	2.75	4.00
S1285	1952S	....	13,707,800	—	—	3.50
a	1952S	micro. double date & MM	—	1.25	4.00	7.00
S1287	1953D	....	56,112,000	—	—	1.50
a	1953D	mustache, die break	—	—	1.00	3.50
S1289	1954	....	54,645,000	—	—	1.00
a	1954	(BIE) LIBERTY	—	1.00	3.50	6.00
b	1954	reverse R in date (die br.) in front of 9..	—	1.00	5.00	9.75
c	1954	Triple Date....................................	—	15.00	40.00	85.00
31290	1954D	....	46,305,000	—	—	1.00
a	1954D	double MM....................................	—	.75	2.75	4.00
S1291	1954S	....	11,834,000	—	—	3.00
a	1954S	double MM....................................	—	.75	3.00	5.50

REVER3E R

1954 QUARTER TRIPLE STRUCK DATE

1956 QUARTER DOUBLE BAR 5

1961 DOUBLE MM

Index #	Date	Description	Mintage	Good	Fine	Unc.
S1294	1956	....	44,813,000	—	—	.75
a	1956	double bar 5..................................	—	1.00	2.50	4.00
S1297	1957D	....	77,924,000	—	—	.50
a	1957D	double MM....................................	—	—	1.50	3.00
S1299	1958D	....	78,124,900	—	—	.50
a	1958D	micro. double LIBERTY & MM..........	—	.50	1.00	2.00
b	1958D	double bar 5..................................	—	1.00	2.75	4.50
S1301	1959D	....	62,054,000	—	—	.50
a	1959D	double MM....................................	—	—	—	1.25
S1303	1960D	....	63,000,000	—	—	.50
a	1960D	double MM....................................	—	—	—	1.25
b	1960D	missing neck muscle & pigtail	—	—	1.00	4.00
c	1960D	micro double motto & date	—	—	2.00	4.00

QUARTERS

Index #	Date	Description	Mintage	Good	Fine	Unc.
S1305	1961D	....	83,656,000	—	—	.50
a	1961D	slash mark die br. (I/N) GOD WE TRUST........................	—	—	1.00	3.00
b	1961D	double MM..............................	—	—	.50	1.25
c	1961D	triple MM................................	—	—	1.00	3.00
S1306	1962	....	39,374,000	—	—	.50
a	1962	proof, micro. double LIBERTY	—	PROOF	10.00	—
S1307	1962D	....	127,554,000	—	—	.50
a	1962D	double MM..............................	—	—	—	1.25
b	1962D	triple MM................................	—	—	—	3.00
c	1962D	micro. double motto & date	—	—	—	4.50
S1309	1963D	....	135,288,000	—	—	.35
a	1963D	micro. double MM.......................	—	—	—	.75
S1311	1964D	....	—	—	—	.35
a	1964D	micro. double MM.......................	—	—	—	.50
S1312	1964P	....	559,700,400	—	—	.35
a	1964P	die break tip of nose vertical, also at top of bust......................	—	—	—	.75
b	1964	Frosted Proof..........................	3,950,762	—	—	6.00

The clad coin series started with the year 1965. The composition of the 1965 quarter is 75% copper alloyed with 25% nickel bonded on a pure copper core.

S1312-5	1965					
a	1965	micro shift lettering rev............................	—	—	—	1.00
	1966					

1964
DIE BREAKS

1964
**LAMINATED
PEEL TYPE**

**FILLED
DIE
QUARTER**

HIGH-LOW MINT MARK

80

Index #	Date	Description	Mintage	Good	Fine	Unc.

FLOWING HAIR TYPE HALF DOLLAR 1794-1795

1795 FLOWING HAIR TYPE (Small Eagle)

Index #	Date	Description	Mintage	Good	Fine	Unc.
S1313	1794	flowing hair type	5,300	260.00	550.00	—
S1314	1795		317,844	125.00	300.00	—
a	1795	two leaves under wing	—	125.00	300.00	—
b	1795	three leaves under wing, recut date	—	300.00	800.00	—
c	1795	STATES originally cut as STETES then A recut/E two leaves under wing	—	375.00	500.00	—
d	1795	recut LIBERTY	—	275.00	500.00	—
e	1795	clash die, UNITED incused under LIBERTY	—	125.00	275.00	—
S1315	1796	15 stars (no mintage known)	—	1200.00	2800.00	—
a	1796	16 stars	—	1200.00	2800.00	—
b	1796	recut 6	—	1200.00	2800.00	—

1803 HERALDIC EAGLE

Index #	Date	Description	Mintage	Good	Fine	Unc.
S1319	1803	large 3	31,715	50.00	85.00	450.00
a	1803	small 3	—	75.00	125.00	560.00
S1320	1805		211,722	35.00	75.00	300.00
a	1805/4	overdate	—	70.00	135.00	450.00
S1321	1806/5	knob 6, all types	839,576	40.00	75.00	400.00
a	1806/	over inverted 6	—	70.00	130.00	600.00
b	1806	round top 6, large stars	—	28.00	60.00	220.00
c	1806	round top 6, small stars	—	30.00	65.00	220.00
d	1806	pointed top 6, stem through claw	—	28.00	65.00	220.00
e	1806	pointed top 6, stem not through claw	—	28.00	65.00	220.00
f	1806	pointed top 6, double T and Y of LIBERTY	—	20.00	55.00	225.00
g	1806	round top 6, recut date	—	32.00	70.00	200.00
h	1806	knob 6, recut 6	—	32.00	70.00	200.00
i	1806	pointed top 6, stem through claw Q zero (18Q6) double T in LIBERTY	—	50.00	95.00	300.00
S1322	1807	bust type facing right	301,076	25.00	55.00	210.00

Index #	Date	Description	Mintage	Good	Fine	Unc.

1806
POINTED 6

DOUBLE T
AND Y

TURBAN HEAD TYPE, BUST FACING LEFT

Index #	Date	Description	Mintage	Good	Fine	Unc.
S1323	1807	small stars	750,500	20.00	45.00	300.00
a	1807	large stars	—	18.00	35.00	215.00
b	1807	50/20 C. reverse side, dot left of shield	—	20.00	40.00	275.00
c	1807	recut 7	—	19.00	40.00	280.00
S1324	1808		1,368,000	9.00	18.00	90.00
a	1808	wide space date (1 8 08	—	12.00	35.00	95.00
b	1808/7	overdate, die break under date	—	12.00	35.00	115.00
c	1808/7	overdate, LIKERTY filled die variety	—	16.00	45.00	122.00
d	1808	rotated reverse	—	12.00	29.00	90.00
S1325	1809		1,405,810	9.00	16.00	100.00

1808
8 OVER 7
DIEBREAK UNDER DATE

1809
DOUBLE
DATE AND
STARS

REVERSE

Index #	Date	Description	Mintage	Good	Fine	Unc.
a	1809	recut date and stars	—	27.00	108.00	325.00
b	1809	recut (U)—(N) of UNITED	—	10.00	18.00	110.00
S1326	1810		1,276,276	8.00	16.00	90.00
a	1810	inverted 8, reverse has clash die marks	—	12.00	45.00	100.00
b	1810	recut date	—	12.00	45.00	100.00
c	1810	reverse side, 50 C shows (5QC) variety	—	13.00	48.00	105.00
S1327	1811	small date, all types	1,203,644	7.00	15.00	85.00
a	1811	large date	—	8.00	17.00	120.00
b	1811	dot variety (18.11)	—	10.00	19.00	130.00
c	1811	recut date (81)	—	10.00	19.00	125.00
S1328	1812		1,628,059	6.75	15.00	95.00
a	1812/11	overdate	—	15.00	22.00	165.00
b	1812	double profile, recut (O) of 50 C	—	12.00	17.50	105.00
c	1812	clashed die variety	—	12.00	17.50	105.00
d	1812	wide date, edge collar shift reads HALF DOLLARIFTY	—	12.00	17.50	105.00

HALF DOLLARS

1813
CLASHED
DIE

1814
OFF
CENTER

Index #	Date	Description	Mintage	Good	Fine	Unc.
S1329	1813		1,241,903	7.00	14.00	70.00
a	1813	double profile	—	8.75	16.00	75.00
b	1813	shifted edge collar, "OR HALA DOLLAR"	—	8.75	16.00	75.00
c	1813	shifted edge collar, "OR HAAL DOLLAR"	—	8.75	16.00	75.00
d	1813	various clash die types, obv-rev	—	9.00	18.00	75.00
e	1813	double clash die "UNUM PLURIBUS" shows between date and bust	—	12.00	21.00	80.00
f	1813	rounded stars	—	7.00	14.00	70.00
g	1813	pointed stars	—	7.00	14.00	70.00
S1330	1814		1,039,075	8.00	15.50	95.00
a	1814/13	overdate, double nose	—	16.50	45.00	150.00
b	1814/13	clash die varieties	—	13.00	35.00	130.00
S1331	1815/12	overdates only	47,150	80.00	160.00	650.00
S1332	1817		1,215,567	7.00	14.00	70.00
a	1817/13	overdate	—	18.00	36.00	140.00
b	1817/14	overdate	rare	VERY RARE		
c	1817	punctuated date (181.7)	—	13.00	35.00	125.00
d	1817	punctuated date (181.7) & double profile	—	17.00	45.50	135.00
e	1817	irregular spacing (1 817)	—	13.00	34.00	124.00

1818
FIRST 18 OVER 17

1819
19 OVER 18
SMALL 9

S1333	1818		1,960,322	5.50	12.75	65.00
a	1818/17	flat top first 8	—	9.50	18.00	67.00
b	1818/17	clash die varieties	—	10.00	19.00	65.00
S1334	1819		2,208,000	7.00	11.00	65.00
a	1819/18	small 9	—	8.00	12.75	65.00
b	1819/18	large 9	—	8.00	12.75	65.00
c	1819/18	irregular spacing (1 81 9)	—	9.00	14.00	60.00
d	1819	double profile, clash die variety	—	9.00	14.50	62.00
e	1819	recut 5 in (50C)	—	7.75	12.75	50.00
S1335	1820	small date, all types	751,122	9.00	16.00	95.00
a	1820	large date	—	9.00	16.00	95.00
b	1820/18	overdate	—	—	—	—
c	1820/19		—	11.00	20.00	90.00
d	1820	curl 2	—	—	—	—
e	1820	knob 2	—	—	—	—
S1337	1822		1,559,573	6.75	12.00	50.00

Index #	Date	Description	Mintage	Good	Fine	Unc.

1828 KNOB ON TOP OF 2 CURLED BASE

1823 23 OVER 22

Index #	Date	Description	Mintage	Good	Fine	Unc.
a	1822/1	overdate	—	40.00	78.00	235.00
S1338	1823		1,694,200	6.00	11.00	46.00
a	1823/22	broken 3	—	35.00	75.00	190.00
b	1823/22	ugly 3	—	11.00	25.00	65.00
c	1823/22	patched 3	—	18.00	35.00	90.00

1823 23 OVER PATCHED 3

1824 4 OVER VARIOUS DATES

Index #	Date	Description	Mintage	Good	Fine	Unc.
S1339	1824		3,504,000	5.75	11.50	48.00
a	1824/	various dates	—	8.00	13.00	50.00
b	1824/21		—	8.00	13.00	60.00
S1340	1825		2,943,000	8.00	13.00	45.00
a	1825	double profile	—	9.00	17.00	55.00
b	1825	triple recut neck	—	9.00	17.00	55.00
c	1825	recut (50 C) reverse	—	9.00	17.00	55.00
d	1825	irregular date (1 82 5)	—	8.00	14.00	39.00
S1341	1826		4,004,000	7.00	12.00	48.00
a	1826	double profile & bust	—	8.00	16.00	50.00
S1342	1827	square base 2	5,493,000	6.50	9.00	48.00
a	1827/6	overdate	—	15.00	30.00	110.00
b	1827	curled 2	—	13.00	30.00	110.00
c	1827	clash die varieties	—	10.00	19.00	39.00
S1343	1828		3,075,000	9.00	13.00	42.00
a	1828	curled base 2, without top knob	—	9.50	15.00	50.00
b	1828	curled base 2, knob top (scarce)	—	38.00	75.00	175.00
c	1828	large 8, square base 2	—	7.00	11.00	52.00
d	1828	small 8, square base 2	—	7.00	11.00	45.00
S1344	1829		3,712,000	5.00	9.00	46.50
a	1829/27	overdate	—	8.50	14.00	50.00
S1345	1830		4,764,000	4.00	7.75	45.00
a	1830	large zero in date	—	6.00	10.00	45.00
b	1830	recut 5 (50 C)	—	7.00	13.00	35.00
S1347	1832	small letters	4,797,000	4.00	8.00	48.00
a	1832	large letters	—	5.00	10.00	49.50
b	1832-1832	(die break—)	—	15.00	45.00	100.00
c	1832	edge collar shift, "OR ALF A DOLLAR"	—	8.50	16.00	40.00
d	1832	edge collar shift, "ORRALF A DOLLAR"	—	8.50	16.00	40.00
e	1832	edge collar shift, "OR H A DOLLAR"	—	8.50	16.00	40.00

HALF DOLLARS

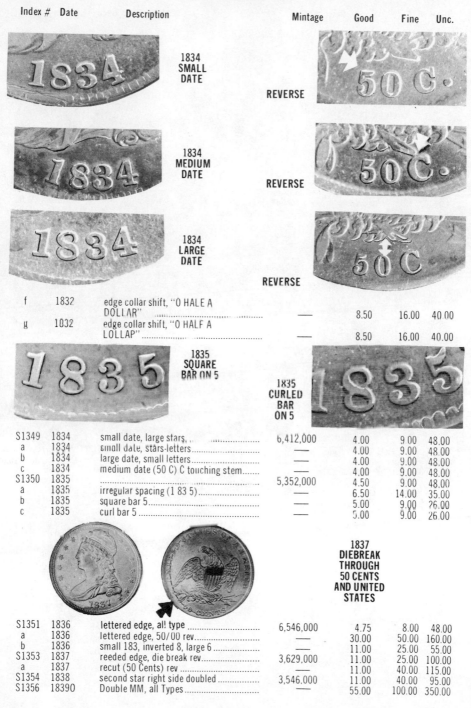

Index #	Date	Description	Mintage	Good	Fine	Unc.

1834 SMALL DATE — REVERSE

1834 MEDIUM DATE — REVERSE

1834 LARGE DATE — REVERSE

Index #	Date	Description	Mintage	Good	Fine	Unc.
f	1832	edge collar shift, "O HALE A DOLLAR"	—	8.50	16.00	40.00
g	1832	edge collar shift, "O HALF A LOLLAP"	—	8.50	16.00	40.00

1835 SQUARE BAR ON 5

1835 CURLED BAR ON 5

Index #	Date	Description	Mintage	Good	Fine	Unc.
S1349	1834	small date, large stars,	6,412,000	4.00	9.00	48.00
a	1834	small date, stars-letters	—	4.00	9.00	48.00
b	1834	large date, small letters	—	4.00	9.00	48.00
c	1834	medium date (50 C) C touching stem	—	4.00	9.00	48.00
S1350	1835		5,352,000	4.50	9.00	48.00
a	1835	irregular spacing (1 83 5)	—	6.50	14.00	35.00
b	1835	square bar 5	—	5.00	9.00	26.00
c	1835	curl bar 5	—	5.00	9.00	26.00

1837 DIEBREAK THROUGH 50 CENTS AND UNITED STATES

Index #	Date	Description	Mintage	Good	Fine	Unc.
S1351	1836	lettered edge, all type	6,546,000	4.75	8.00	48.00
a	1836	lettered edge, 50/00 rev	—	30.00	50.00	160.00
b	1836	small 183, inverted 8, large 6	—	11.00	25.00	55.00
S1353	1837	reeded edge, die break rev	3,629,000	11.00	25.00	100.00
a	1837	recut (50 Cents) rev	—	11.00	40.00	115.00
S1354	1838	second star right side doubled	3,546,000	11.00	40.00	95.00
S1356	18390	Double MM, all Types	—	55.00	100.00	350.00

Index #	Date	Description	Mintage	Good	Fine	Unc.

LIBERTY SEATED HALF DOLLARS 1839-1891

1840 MICRO O

Index #	Date	Description	Mintage	Good	Fine	Unc.
S1358	18400	micro. MM	855,000	8.00	15.00	70.00
a	18400	large O, MM	—	7.00	12.00	57.50
S1359	1840		1,435,000	5.00	11.00	52.00
a	1840	reverse of 1838, large letters	—	5.50	11.00	52.00
b	1840	reverse of 1838, small letters	—	5.50	11.00	52.00
c	1840	recut 18	—	6.00	12.00	56.00
S1360	1841		310,000	8.00	14.00	65.00
a	1841	recut date	—	10.00	18.00	75.00
S1361	1842	small date, all types	2,012,000	4.00	12.00	50.00
a	1842	large date	—	4.00	12.00	50.00
b	1842	recut date	—	9.00	14.00	60.00
S1363	1843		3,844,000	4.50	9.50	50.00
a	1843	recut date	—	6.50	12.00	55.00
S1364	1844		1,766,000	4.50	9.50	45.00
a	1844	recut date	—	7.00	14.00	50.00
S1365	18440		2,005,000	4.75	12.00	48.00
a	18440	recut date	—	6.00	14.00	55.00

1844 RECUT DATE

1846 6/OVER HORIZONTAL 6

Index #	Date	Description	Mintage	Good	Fine	Unc.
S1368	1846	small date, all type	2,110,000	4.50	12.00	48.00
a	1846	tall date	—	4.50	12.00	50.00
b	1846/	horizontal 6 placement error	—	45.00	90.00	260.00
S1369	18460	small date	2,304,000	4.50	10.00	50.00
a	18460	tall date	—	25.00	55.00	195.00
S1370	1847		1,156,000	4.50	10.00	48.00
a	1847/46	overdate	—	140.00	260.00	800.00
S1372	1848		580,000	4.50	10.00	48.00
a	1848	recut stars	—	6.00	11.00	50.00
S1376	1849		1,252,000	4.50	10.00	48.00
a	1849	recut date	—	8.50	19.00	55.00
S1378	1850		227,000	20.00	45.00	120.00
a	1850	recut date, stars & LIBERTY	—	25.00	55.00	150.00
S1380	1851		200,750	10.00	26.00	120.00
a	1851	recut stars	—	12.00	30.00	120.00
b	1851	die break left of 1	—	10.00	26.00	110.00
S1382	1853	Recut arrows and dot	—	8.00	20.00	100.00
S1393	18560		2,658,000	4.00	10.00	48.00
a	18560	double stars	—	5.00	12.00	45.00
S1395	1857		1,988,000	4.50	10.00	48.00
a	1857	recut date	—	6.50	14.00	45.00

1853 LIBERTY HALF DOLLAR RECUT ARROWS AND DOT

1859 "HALE" DOLLAR

Index #	Date	Description	Mintage	Good	Fine	Unc.
S1403	1859S	....	566,000	8.00	25.00	90.00
a	1859S	HALE DOL., collar shift	—	9.00	30.00	90.00
S1415	1864S	large MM	658,000	4.50	9.00	50.00
a	1864	small MM	—	4.50	9.00	50.00
S1416	1865	....	—	5.00	10.00	48.00
a	1865/1865	inverted date	511,900	45.00	80.00	225.00
S1433	1872CC		272,000	30.00	70.00	300.00
a	1872CC	18722 double 2	rare	65.00	175.00	850.00
S1435	1873	closed 3	801,000	5.00	11.00	45.00
a	1873	open 3	—	9.00	25.00	80.00
S1449	1877S		5,356,000	4.50	11.00	42.00
a	1877S	double MM	—	6.00	18.00	65.00

BARBER OR LIBERTY HEAD TYPE 1892-1915

BARBER TYPE HALF DOLLAR

Index #	Date	Description	Mintage	Good	Fine	Unc.
S1467	1892O	medium MM	390,000	25.00	40.00	110.00
a	1892O	micro. MM	—	35.00	50.00	125.00
S1474	1894S		4,048,000	3.50	12.00	100.00
a	1894S	recut U. S. AMERICA	—	5.00	11.50	125.00
S1486	1898S		2,358,000	3.75	10.00	100.00
a	1898S	recut legend	—	4.00	14.00	120.00

HALF DOLLARS

Index #	Date	Description	Mintage	Good	Fine	Unc.

LIBERTY WALKING HALF DOLLARS 1916-1947

Designed by A. A. Weinman, his initials are under tip of wing feathers (Rev.) On dates 1916 thru 1917 MM is under motto In God We Trust. Also Rev. to the left bottom rim.

Index #	Date	Description	Mintage	Good	Fine	Unc.
S1547	1918S		10,282,000	1.50	4.00	100.00
a	1918S	double MM	—	3.50	10.00	100.00
S1548	1919		962,000	3.00	9.50	230.00
a	1919	clash die, obv. over motto	—	4.00	15.00	125.00
S1549	1919D		1,165,000	3.50	10.00	360.00
a	1919D	double MM	—	3.00	12.50	400.00
S1550	1919S		1,552,000	4.00	14.00	490.00
a	1919S	clash dies	—	5.00	26.00	600.00
S1551	1920		6,372,000	1.00	4.00	50.00
a	1920	clash dies, (trust to foot)	—	2.00	7.50	75.00

1920 **CLASH DIES**

1943 **DOUBLE DATE**

Index #	Date	Description	Mintage	Good	Fine	Unc.
S1564	1934D		2,361,000	.75	2.00	24.00
a	1934D	micro. MM	—	.75	2.00	24.00
b	1934D	large MM	—	.75	2.00	24.00
S1565	1934S		3,652,000	.75	2.00	50.00
a	1934S	double profile, motto & flag	—	2.00	9.00	38.00
S1577	1939		6,820,000	—	1.50	9.00
a	1939	double motto, obv., double HALF DOLLAR, rev.	—	6.50	25.00	50.00
S1583	1941D		11,248,400	—	—	12.00
a	1941D	plugged o in (God)	—	—	—	17.50
S1588	1943	double date	—	6.00	25.00	50.00
S1591	1944		28,206,000	—	—	5.00
a	1944	die break appears as (194C4)	—	1.50	6.00	15.00
S1593	1944S		8,904,000	—	—	7.00
a	1944S	double MM	—	—	6.00	15.00
S1594	1945		31,502,000	—	2.00	5.00
a	1945	double die shift rev	—	—	6.00	25.00
S1601	1947D		3,900,000	—	—	7.50
a	1947D	double HALF DOLLAR, rev.	—	.75	2.00	14.00

FRANKLIN HALF DOLLARS 1948-1963

Index #	Date	Description	Mintage	Good	Fine	Unc.
S1603	1948D	....	4,028,000	.80	1.50	7.50
a	1948D	micro. double MM............................	—	1.00	3.50	14.00
S1605	1949D		4,120,000	.80	1.50	11.00
a	1949D	clog MM..	—	1.00	3.00	15.00
S1608	1950D		8,031,000	—	—	8.00
a	1950D	micro. double MM............................	—	1.00	3.00	18.00
S1609	1951		16,859,602	—	.75	3.75
a	1951	bugs bunny, clash die at mouth...............	—	—	1.50	9.50
S1613	1952D		25,395,000	—	—	2.25
a	1952D	micro. double MM............................	—	1.00	2.00	9.50
S1615	1953	.... proofs	(128,000)	PROOF	20.00	
a	1953	proof filled die, missing feathers, eagle....	—	30.00	—	—
S1616	1953D		20,900,000	—	—	2.00
a	1953D	clog MM	—	—	1.00	8.50
S1617	1953S		4,148,000	—	1.15	5.00
a	1953S	double profile & MM.........................	—	—	4.50	14.00
S1619	1954D		25,445,000	—	—	2.00
a	1954D	micro. double MM............................	—	—	3.50	8.00
b	1954D	micro double MM, and lettering, rev.	—	1.50	4.50	7.75
S1620	1954S		4,993,000	—	—	4.00
a	1954S	micro. double MM, die br. thru PLURIBUS to eagle..............................	—	1.25	4.75	14.00
S1621	1955	....	2,876,000	5.75	8.00	10.00
a	1955	bugs bunny, variety............................	—	5.00	7.00	12.00
b	1955	bugs bunny, hyphen under 1..................	—	6.00	8.00	14.00

1955
BUGS
BUNNY
DIEBREAK
AT MOUTH

Index #	Date	Description	Mintage	Good	Fine	Unc.
S1624	1957D	....	19,966,000	—	—	1.75
a	1957D	double lettering & MM........................	—	—	2.50	5.00
b	1957D	R of TRUST connected to bust..............	—	—	3.00	6.50
S1626	1958D		23,962,000	—	—	1.50
a	1958D	double motto & MM..........................	—	—	3.50	6.50
b	1958D	double chin...................................	—	—	2.50	4.00
c	1958D	joined R and Bust	—	1.25	2.50	5.75

1957
JOINED
R AND BUST

HALF
DOLLAR
RIIBUS

HALF DOLLARS

Index #	Date	Description	Mintage	Good	Fine	Unc.
S1627	1959		7,349,000	—	—	3.50
a	1959	double chin	—	—	2.00	4.50
S1628	1959D		13,053,000	—	—	1.75
a	1959D	double MM, die br. thru PLURIBUS	—	—	1.50	4.00
b	1959D	double date	—	—	3.50	6.75
c	1959D	micro double MM, and lettering, rev.	—	1.00	3.50	6.50
S1630	1960D		18,215,000	—	—	1.50
a	1960D	double lettering & MM	—	—	1.00	4.00
S1632	1961D		20,276,000	—	—	1.50
a	1961D	double MM	—	—	1.00	3.50
S1633	1962		12,932,000	—	—	2.00
a	1962	recut LIBERTY	—	—	1.00	3.50
S1634	1962D		35,473,000	—	—	1.25
a	1962D	double MM	—	—	1.00	1.75
b	1962D	double motto & MM	—	—	1.25	3.00
c	1962D	double U. S. AMERICA	—	—	1.00	2.50
d	1962D	Bar E	—	—	—	2.50
e	1962D	double MM & yoke of bell	—	—	1.00	3.00
S1635	1963	proofs	(3,075,645)	—	PROOF	4.00
a	1963	proof thin date	—	—	PROOF	5.00
b	1963		25,239,645	—	—	1.25
S1636	1963D		67,069,292	—	—	.85
a	1963D	clapper bar missing	—	—	—	2.50
b	1963D	micro shift reverse, double MM	—	—	—	3.75

TYPE 1

TYPE 2

TYPE 3

The 3 types of Eagles on the reverse of the Franklin halves appears to become an interest future variety. Much study is needed to present an accurate survey and values. The next edition will elaborate fully with values.

Type 1 Low relief. Four flattened feathers to left of eagle's perch. Separate feathers in upper regions of lower feathers.
Type 2 Eagle in high relief. Three feathers to left of eagle's perch.
Type 3 Eagle in low relief. Three feathers to left of perch.
Inscription noted on the Liberty Bell reads Pass and Stow, the name of firm that cast the bell, Philadelphia and date.

Type 1	1956	(proof)	rare	18.00
Type 1	1958	reg. issue	scarce	14.00
Type 2	1958	reg. issue	rare	18.00
Type 2	1959	reg. issue	common	4.50
Type 3	1959	reg. issue	scarce	6.50

**1964 D
TRUST   DOUBLED**

**1964 KENNEDY
HALF DOLLAR**

Index #	Date	Description	Mintage	Good	Fine	Unc.
S1637	1964	....	235,581,000	—	—	.75
a	1964	die break, 196.4, dot..............	—	—	—	1.75
b	1964	shifted lettering on rev.	—	—	—	2.00
c	1964	struck on quarter blank	—	—	—	75.00
d	1964	proof shifted lettering on rev.	156,205,000	—	—	15.00
e	1964	proof frosted	—	—	—	12.00
f	1964	dot on throat	—	—	—	1.25
S1638	1964D		—	—	—	.75
a	1964D	double lettering on rev.	—	—	—	2.00
b	1964D	double MM	—	—	—	2.00
c	1964D	various filled die, rev.	—	—	—	1.50
d	1964D	struck on a dime blank, rare............	—	—	—	250.00
e	1964D	filled die R, LIBERTY...............	—	—	—	2.00
f	1964D	micro shift in God (WE TRUST).............	—	—	—	3.50
g	1964D	dot right bottom 6..................	—	—	—	2.00

The clad coins series started with the year 1965. The composition of the contents are as follows: 1965 half dollar has 80% silver alloyed with 20% copper, bonded on a core of $21\frac{1}{2}$% silver and $78\frac{1}{2}$% copper. An overall base of 40% silver. The former half dollar consisted of 90% silver.

S1638-5	1965		—	—	—	.75
a	1965	micro shift letters, rev.............	—	—	—	1.50

STRUCK ON SCRAP METAL

SILVER DOLLARS 1794-1935

1795
FLOWING HAIR
TYPE

Index #	Date	Description	Mintage	Good	Fine	Unc.
S1639	1795	flowing hair, two leaves under wing.........	—	200.00	275.00	1400.00
a	1795	three leaves under wing...........................	—	200.00	275.00	1400.00
b	1795	tied bundle hair, small eagle....................	—	135.00	230.00	1200.00
S1640	1796	small date, sm. letters............................	72,920	105.00	200.00	1100.00
a	1796	small date, large letters..........................	—	105.00	200.00	1100.00
b	1796	large date, sm. letters............................	—	105.00	200.00	1100.00
S1641	1797	9 stars left, 7 stars right.........................	7,776	135.00	300.00	1350.00
a	1797	10 stars left, 6 stars right........................	—	155.00	300.00	1350.00
S1642	1798	15 stars..	327,536	135.00	240.00	1100.00
a	1798	13 stars..	—	140.00	225.00	1000.00
b	1798	large heraldic eagle, knob 9....................	—	75.00	140.00	550.00

1799 DRAPED BUST TYPE　　　　　　　　　1804 RARE COIN

Index #	Date	Description	Mintage	Good	Fine	Unc.
S1643	1799	over 98 rev., 15 stars.............................	423,515	80.00	135.00	600.00
a	1799	over 98 rev., 13 stars.............................	—	75.00	125.00	600.00
b	1799	irregular date, 13 or 15 stars...................	—	70.00	120.00	480.00
c	1799	perfect date..	—	70.00	120.00	460.00
S1644	1800	recut letters obv.	220,920	50.00	100.00	400.00
a	1800	recut letters rev....................................	—	50.00	100.00	400.00
b	1800	AMERICAI, die br....................................	—	60.00	115.00	440.00
c	1800	dotted date..	—	50.00	110.00	425.00
S1646	1802/1	overdate..	41,650	60.00	110.00	425.00
a	1802/1	double profile, wings	—	60.00	110.00	425.00
S1647	1803	large 3..	66,064	50.00	100.00	400.00
a	1803	small 3..	—	50.00	100.00	400.00
S1648	1804 *	original, has beaded edge denticles..........	rare	—		29,000.00
a	1804 *	restrike,...	—	—	—	—

* This issue is believed struck after 1836, elongated denticle edge were used prior to this date. The Gobrecht Dollar of 1836 was the first to have this type of beaded denticle edge due to new process of minting.

DOLLARS

Silver Dollars Liberty or Morgan Type 1878-1921

1878 DOUBLE DATE STARS AND LIBERTY

Designed by George T. Morgan, his initials are noted above date under neck (M) also on the reverse on the left loop of ribbon. Difficult to see, the M appears vertical. Several are known to have a dot above the initials and are rare especially when both sides include these. This is a method used to keep tabs of changed dies.

Index #	Date	Description	Mintage	Good	Fine	Unc.
S1696	1878	....	10,093,000	—	—	2./5
a	1878	10 feathers, also known as 7/3 feathers	—	—	3.50	16.00
b	1878	13 feathers 8/5 feathers	—	—	3.50	16.00
c	1878	12 feathers 7/5 feathers	—	—	3.50	16.00
d	1878	double LIBERTY			—	—
e	1878	filled die curl near M above date			—	3.75
f	1878	various curved ear lobes			3.50	6.50
g	1878	double date, stars, and D of dollar, dot U, doubled			4.75	9.75
h	1878	various filled die lettering rev			~3.00	4.50
i	1878	various clog lettering			3.00	5.00
j	1878	large nose, weak bridge			—	12.00
S1697	1878CC	....	2,212,000	—	4.50	12.00
a	1878CC	double leaves, date & stars		—	9.00	18.00
b	1878CC	rotated rev. die	—	—	4.00	16.00
S1698	1878S	....	9,774,000	—	—	2.75
a	1878S	tongue in lip	—	—	2.75	9.00
b	1878S	fill die (TIUST)	—	—	1.75	4.75
S1699	1879	....	14,807,000	—	—	2.75
a	1879	recut 7	—	—	2.75	5.75

1878 S TONGUE IN LIP

1879 S DOUBLE S

Index #	Date	Description	Mintage	Good	Fine	Unc.
S1701	18790	large MM	2,877,000	—	—	4.75
a	18790	small MM	—	—	—	4.75
S1702	1879S	....	9,110,000	—	—	2.50
a	1879S	double MM	—	—	3.50	9.00
S1703	1879CC	....	756,000	—	11.00	165.00
a	1879CC	double MM	—	—	14.00	180.00
b	1879CC	recut 18	—	—	14.00	175.00
c	1879CC	large CC/ small CC	—	—	15.00	180.00
S1704	1880CC	....	591,000	—	17.00	50.00
a	1880CC	small MM	—	—	20.00	60.00
b	1880CC	large MM	—	—	20.00	60.00
c	1880CC	/79	—	—	40.00	125.00
d	1880CC/79	7 shows only	—	—	30.00	70.00
e	1880CC/79	top of 7 shows only	—	—	25.00	65.00

93

DOLLARS

Index #	Date	Description	Mintage	Good	Fine	Unc.
S1705	1880	....	12,601,000	—	—	4.00
a	1880	recut 80	—	—	2.75	5.75
S1706	1880S	....	8,900,000	—	—	3.50
a	1880S	double MM	—	—	4.50	8.00
b	1880S	double date..	—	—	4.00	10.00
c	1880S	large MM	—	—	—	3.00
d	1880S	small MM	—	—	—	3.00
S1707	1881	....	9,163,000	—	—	2.50
a	1881	filled die curl near M	—	—	—	3.00
b	1881	recut lettering on rev..................................	—	—	1.50	3.75
S1710	1881S	....	—	—	—	2.50
a	1881S	double MM..	—	—	2.50	5.50
S1713	18820	....	6,090,000	—	—	4.75
a	18820	double MM, O/S	—	—	17.00	40.00
b	18820	double MM, O/broken O	—	—	5.00	16.00
c	18820	open knob 2	—	—	4.00	10.00
d	18820	closed knob 2	—	—	4.00	10.00

1884 DOT NEXT TO M

1888 O DOUBLE PROFILE

Index #	Date	Description	Mintage	Good	Fine	Unc.
S1714	1882S	....	9,250,000	—	—	3.00
a	1882S	recut 88	—	—	2.75	5.50
S1719	1884	....	14,070,000	—	—	3.00
a	1884	dot next to M, near curl above date..........	—	—	5.75	40.00
b	1884	dot next to M, near bow on rev..............	—	—	5.75	40.00
c	1884	dot next to M, obv.—rev. Bow..............	Rare	—	15.00	85.00
S1720	18840	....	9,730,000	—	—	2.75
a	18840	oval MM	—	—	—	3.00
b	18840	round MM	—	—	—	3.00
c	18840	double MM, O/small O	—	—	—	6.50
d	18840	O over unidentified verticle line..............	—	—	—	—
S1725	18850	....	9,185,000	—	—	2.50
a	18850	filled die curl near M	—	—	—	3.00
S1731	18870	....	11,550,000	—	2.50	5.00
a	18870	recut 7	—	—	4.50	9.00
S1733	1888P	....	19,183,833	—	—	2.00
a	1888P	Spike Mouth (Clash Die)	—	—	—	6.75
S1734	18880	....	12,150,000	—	—	2.50
a	18880	double profile	—	—	8.00	30.00
S1735	1888S	....	657,000	—	25.00	40.00
a	1888S	double letters rev. also filled die..............	—	—	35.00	50.00
S1737	1889CC	....	350,000	40.00	80.00	700.00
a	1889CC	most of obv. double & part rev.............	—	50.00	95.00	800.00
b	1889CC	double struck, obv.-rev.	—	—	—very rare	
S1738	18890	....	11,875,000	—	2.50	10.00
a	18890	reverse rotated die, 45 degrees..............	—	—	—	—
b	18890	"E" under Eagles tail left, clash dies	—	—	4.50	11.00
S1741	1890CC	....	2,309,041	—	9.00	35.00
a	1890CC	recut 9	—	—	10.00	37.00

DOLLARS

Index #	Date	Description	Mintage	Good	Fine	Unc.
S1742	18900	....	10,701,000	—	—	7.00
a	18900	double MM...	—	—	4.00	15.00

CLASH DIE, E UNDER EAGLES TAIL

Index #	Date	Description	Mintage	Good	Fine	Unc.
S1746	18910	....	7,954,000	—	—	7.00
a	18910	clash die, E under eagles tail....................	—	—	3.00	10.00
S1752	1893	....	378,792	—	10.00	47.00
a	1893	double stars..	—	—	12.00	85.00
S1/62	18950	....	450,000	—	11.00	160.00
a	18950	recut 5	—	—	12.00	175.00
31763	18960	small MM...	4,900,000	—	—	16.00
a	18960	large MM...	—	—	—	16.00
b	18960	recut 6...	—	—	4.00	14.00
S1773	18990	small MM...	12,290,000	—	—	2.50
a	18990	large MM...	—	—	—	3.00
b	18990	circular die Br..	—	—	—	5.50
S1776	19000	small MM...	12,590,000	—	—	2.50
a	19000	large MM...	—	—	—	3.00
b	19000	circular die br. thru U.S. AMERICA...........	—	—	—	4.50
c	19000	double MM, O/O..	—	—	—	9.50
d	19000	double MM, O/CC..	—	—	15.00	35.00
S1778	1901	....	6,962,000	—	2.50	35.00
a	1901	double outline rev. design	—	—	3.50	40.00
S1781	1902	....	7,994,000	—	—	7.75
a	1902	clog bar 2 in date..	—	—	1.50	9.00
S1782	19020	small MM...	8,636,000	—	—	3.50
a	19020	large MM...	—	—	—	3.50
S1786	1903S	small MM...	1,241,000	3.00	8.00	200.00
a	1903S	large MM...	—	3.00	8.00	50.00
S1788	19040	....	3,720,000	—	—	3.00
a	19040	double (IN GOD WE TRUST)	—	—	—	8.00
S1790	1921	Morgan type...	44,690,000	—	—	2.00
a	1921	micro. double lettering............................	—	—	—	4.50
b	1921	eyebrow variety..	—	—	4.50	8.00
c	1921	I.R.'(infrequent recded edge)	—	—	4.50	11.50
S1791	1921D	....	20,345,000	—	—	5.00
a	1921D	shifted left side of eagle............................	—	—	—	7.00
S1792	1921S	....	21,695,000	—	—	6.00
a	1921S	horned dated	—	—	—	12.00
b	1921S	double date, and liberty............................	—	—	5.00	12.00

DOLLARS

1921-MORGAN TYPE I.R. (Infrequently reeded) dollars

The following are the characteristics of this issue:
(1.) All I.R. dollars came from a single reeding collar on a single press. There are 154 reeds per coin as compared with 186+4 (182-190) on other issues. The only coin in any way similar is an 1878-P reeded 168 per coin.
(2.) 10,000 pieces of 1921-P were examined to obtain the frequency which is 91 per 10,000. This corresponds to a mintage of 416,497 coins.
(3.) Of these coins, 166,000 were Type I with the reverse misaligned to the left about 10 degrees, the remainder Type 11 with normally aligned reverse.
(4.) The I.R. dollars were selectively dropped in the North Central area. In this area, hoards run up to, but not above 10% I.R. dollars. This indicates that there were 10 presses operating, of which one struck I.R. dollars.
(5.) There is a definite parallelism between the distribution of high-grade prooflike 1921-P Morgan dollars and I.R. dollars which indicates the I.R. dollars were struck at the beginning of 1921 production.
(6.) By assuming an equal striking per working day in 1921, one can calculate that all the I.R. dollars were struck on the first two working days. Presumably Type 1 was struck one day and Type 11 the next.

ARROWS INDICATE LOCATION OF TWO 1921-P-I.R. DOLLARS

JUDD 1800

The Infrequently Reeded 1921 Philadelphia Morgan dollar. As in the case of the reeded edge cent of 1863 with normal obverse and reverse, Judd 300, the Mint has no records of the purpose of the distinctive edge design. 400,000 pieces were struck, these coins being the first dollars produced in 1921. Normal reeding collars create 188 corrugations per coin, each having detailed micro-structure which appears to show the collar was hand-cut. These 1921-P-I.R.dollars are all from the same reeding collar, with only 154 corrugations per coin. In addition, the corrugations are mere simple notches suggesting the collar was machine cut and that this unusual reeding was actually the first trial, an unsuccessful one, of a machine cut collar for silver dollars.

Like the prooflike 1921-P normally reeded dollars, the 1921-P-I.R. dollars appear, from present distribution, to have been released selectively in the North Central States. Wastage of the issue, considered numismatically unpromising, has made BU specimens quite uncommon and prooflike pieces extremely rare; only 3 are known.

An interesting fact about this dollar is that, as the illustration shows, they can immediately be picked out of a roll of mixed dollars without looking at the date on any of the coins. Thus, this is the only U.S. coin of any issue which is identified not from its obverse or reverse, but from its edge. It is also a regular die trial piece and, as such, the last collectible pattern coin of the United States.

Strictly BU specimens now wholesale at about $4. There has been no sale of a prooflike 1921-P-I.R. Circulated pieces VF to AU generally bring $2.50 to $3.00.

DOLLARS

Index #	Date	Description	Mintage	Good	Fine	Unc.

1921
DESIGNER'S
INITIAL
WITH DOT

1921 SILVER
DOLLAR
DESIGNER INITIAL

Silver Dollars Peace Type 1921-1935

Index #	Date	Description	Mintage	Good	Fine	Unc.
S1793	1921	PEACE TYPE	1,006,000	4.00	12.00	35.00
a	1921	double profile	—	—	13.50	37.00

1922
PEACE
TYPE

1922 DOUBLE DATE

Index #	Date	Description	Mintage	Good	Fine	Unc.
S1794	1922		51,737,000	—	—	2.50
a	1922	mustache type, die br.	—	—	4.00	9.00
b	1922	double profile & date	—	—	3.50	8.00
c	1922	large dangling ear ring, (die break)	—	—	4.50	8.50
d	1922	thin mustache, die break	—	—	4.75	9.50
e	1922	thick mustache, die break	—	—	4.75	9.50
f	1922	type of 1921, note reg. 1921 has 4 rays under ONE, 8 rays under tail. 1922 reg. has 3 rays under ONE, 6 rays under tail.	—	—	10.00	25.00
S1795	1922D		15,063,000	—	—	5.50
a	1922D	double date	—	—	—	9.00
S1796	1922S		17,475,000	—	—	6.00
a	1922S	double date	—	—	—	8.00
S1797	1923		30,800,000	—	—	2.50
a	1923	double date	—	—	—	5.50
S1798	1923D		6,811,000	—	—	11.00
a	1923D	circular die br. obv.	—	—	—	12.00
S1802	1924		11,811,000	—	—	4.50
a	1924	double date	—	—	—	6.75
S1803	1925		10,198,000	—	—	3.00
a	1925	double date	—	—	—	5.75
S1811	1928S		1,632,000	—	—	28.00
a	1928S	double profile & date	—	—	—	33.00
S1813	1934D		1,569,000	—	—	26.00
a	1934D	double date	—	—	—	35.00
b	1934D	double date & profile	—	—	—	40.00
c	1934D	double date, LIBERTY & TRUST	—	—	—	45.00
d	1934D	last ray of Tiara, doubled	—	—	—	34.00
S1815	1935		1,576,000	—	5.50	18.00
a	1935	double date	—	—	—	24.00
S1816	1935S		1,964,000	—	4.50	50.00
a	1935S	extra rays, above-below eagles tail, 4 above, 7 below	—	—	6.50	58.00

Silver Dollars Liberty Seated Type (Gobrecht) 1836-1839

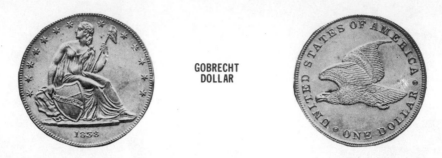

GOBRECHT DOLLAR

Designed by C. Gobrecht. Reverse shows eagle in flight surrounded by stars. A pattern coin never issued officially. Several varieties; plain edge, with and without stars.

1884 TRADE DOLLAR

TRADE DOLLAR 1873-1885 Silver Dollars Liberty Seated Type (regular) 1840-1873

This issue was struck from 1873 to 1885. The Trade Dollar was issued to compete with the Foreign Trade market. Due to declining price of silver bullion, Congress repealed this act and recalled this issue for the melting pot.

This is the only issue known to have been recalled by the government contrary to beliefs of other coinage recalled due to errors and other theories.

The Trade Dollar weighs 420 grains compared to our standard weight regular silver dollars of 412½ grains.

Index #	Date	Description	Mintage	Good	Fine	Unc.
S1827	1876CC	....	509,000	15.00	35.00	95.00
a	1876CC	rev. side, most all double impression	—	18.00	45.00	110.00
S1828	1876S	....	5,227,000	10.00	18.00	40.00
a	1876S	leaves & berries in mid air, small MM, open space leaves on rev., dot after word grain..	—	14.00	30.00	75.00
	1876S	large MM, comma after word grain on rev., short arrow end shaft, close space leaves..	—	14.00	30.00	75.00
S1831	1877S	....	9,519,000	10.00	18.00	40.00
a	1877S	double wing, & U. S. AMERICA................	—	12.00	22.50	55.00

GOLD DOLLARS 1849-1889

TYPE 1 1849-1854 Small size liberty

Index #	Date	Description	Mintage	Good	Fine	Unc.
S1842	1849	open wreath	688,000	—	21.00	55.00
a	1849	closed wreath	—	—	21.00	55.00
S1843	1849C	open wreath	11,634	—	12,000.00	
a	1849C	closed wreath	—	—	120.00	500.00

TYPE 2 1854-1856 large size

Index #	Date	Description	Mintage	Good	Fine	Unc.
S1866	1855		758,269	—	100.00	210.00
a	1855	clash die, obv. shows on rev.	—	—	100.00	210.00
b	1855	recut date	—	—	160.00	225.00
S1869	1855O		—	—	160.00	225.00
a	1855O	recut 1	55,000	—	175.00	275.00
S1870	1856S		—	—	130.00	255.00
a	1856S	double MM	24,600	—	130.00	265.00
b	1856S	double 1 and DOLLAR rev.	—	—	130.00	265.00

TYPE 3 1856 LARGER PORTRAIT

Index #	Date	Description	Mintage	Good	Fine	Unc.
S1871	1856	slant 5	1,762,000	—	25.00	65.00
a	1856	upright 5	—	—	30.00	70.00
S1880	1859		168,000	—	35.00	70.00
a	1859	clash die variety	—	—	36.00	72.00
b	1859	double design & letters	—	—	40.00	35.00
S1887	1861		527,499	—	35.00	60.00
a	1861	clash die variety	—	—	36.00	62.00
b	1861	double 1 and DOLLAR	—	—	40.00	70.00
S1889	1862		1,326,000	—	35.00	68.00
a	1862	double 1 and DOLLAR	—	—	40.00	75.00
S1901	1873	closed 3	—	—	42.00	77.00
a	1873	open 3	—	—	37.00	72.00

$2.50 GOLD PIECES 1796-1929

Index #	Date	Description	Mintage	Good	Fine	Unc.
S1918	1796	no stars	—	—	2500.00	7000.00
a	1796	stars	—	—	2700.00	7500.00
S1921	1802/1		—	—	500.00	2200.00
S1922	1804	13 stars	3,327	—	525.00	2000.00
a	1804	14 stars	—	—	525.00	2000.00
S1924	1806/4		1,616	—	700.00	2500.00
S1925	1806/5		—	—	600.00	2900.00
S1929	1824/21		2,600	—	450.00	2200.00
S1931	1826/25		760	—	575.00	3000.00
S1938	1834	motto above eagle	4,000	—	500.00	1800.00
S1939	1834	no motto above eagle	112,234	—	55.00	135.00
S1962	1843C	small date	26,000	—	125.00	1100.00
a	1843C	large date	—	—	70.00	150.00
S1964	1843O	small date	—	—	45.00	90.00
a	1843O	large date	—	—	70.00	175.00
S1971	1846	recut date	21,598	—	45.00	85.00

GOLD PIECES

Index #	Date	Description	Mintage	Good	Fine	Unc.
S1992	18510	....	148,000	—	30.00	65.00
a	18510	double date................	—	25.00	60.00	150.00
S2029	1862/1	....	—	Rare	—	—
S2040	1867S	....	28,000	—	40.00	280.00
a	1867S	shifted lettering, rev.	—	—	rare	—
S2041	1868S	recut 6	34,000	—	57.00	90.00
S2050	1873	open 3	178,000	—	45.00	68.00
a	1873	closed 3	—	—	45.00	68.00
S2074	1891	....	11,040	—	45.00	100.00
a	1891	shifted lettering rev.	—	—	55.00	120.00

$3.00 GOLD PIECES 1854 - 1889

S2112	1856S	small MM	34,500	—	175.00	260.00
a	1856S	large MM	—	—	175.00	260.00
S2116	1859	recut 19	15,638	—	190.00	270.00
S2119	1861	....	6,072	—	175.00	350.00
a	1861	no neckline................	—	—	rare	—
S2122	1864	recut 18	2,680	—	200.00	270.00
S2127	1869	recut 9	2,625	—	200.00	275.00
S2132	1873	open 3........................	25	—	—	3000.00
a	1873	close 3 all restrikes...	—	—	—	1800.00
S2137	1878/76	(not verified)	—	—	VERY RARE	
S2141	1882/2	....	—	—	250.00	500.00
S2148	1889	double 8....................	2,429	—	250.00	500.00

$4.00 GOLD PIECE 1879 - 1880

$4.00 GOLD—STELLA 1879 FLOWING HAIR TYPE PROOFS ONLY $6,000.00

$5.00 GOLD PIECES 1795 - 1929

 **TURBAN HEAD**

S2151	1795	small eagle................	8,707	—	900.00	2000.00
a	1795	large eagle.................	—	—	1100.00	3500.00
b	1795	States, last S/D, small eagle.................	—	—	—	—

GOLD PIECES

Index #	Date	Description	Mintage	Good	Fine	Unc.

HERALDIC EAGLE

Index #	Date	Description	Mintage	Good	Fine	Unc.
S2152	1796/95	....	—	—	700.00	1900.00
S2153	1797/95	....	—	—	1100.00	2500.00
a	1797	15 stars...............................	—	—	1100.00	3500.00
b	1797	16 stars...............................	—	—	1100.00	3500.00
S2154	1798	small eagle large 8, 13 stars..............	—	—	400.00	1500.
a	1798	large eagle, heraldic large 8, 14 stars......	—	—	550.00	1600.
S2156	1800	....	37,628	—	400.00	900.00
a	1800	small/large M (America)	—	—	—	—
S2157	1802/1	....	53,176	—	350.00	900.00
S2158	1803/2	....	33,506	—	400.00	850.00
S2159	1804	small 8..................................	30,475	—	300.00	700.00
a	1804	large 8..................................	—	—	300.00	700.00
b	1804	small 180 / large 180	—	—	rare	—
S2161	1806	pointed top 6	64,093	—	300.00	700.00
a	1806	round top 6	—	—	300.00	700.00
S2164	1808/7	....	55,578	—	350.00	700.00
S2165	1809/8	....	33,875	—	375.00	800.00
S2167	1810	small date, sm. 5 rev...................	100,287	—	275.00	600.00
a	1810	small date, tall 5 rev..................	—	—	275.00	600.00
b	1810	large date.............................	—	—	275.00	600.00
S2168	1811	small 5 rev.	99,581	—	250.00	575.00
a	1811	large 5 rev.	—	—	250.00	575.00
S2171	1814/13	....	15,454	—	350.00	800.00
S2173	1818	....	48,588	—	450.00	950.00
a	1818	(Statesof) one word	—	—	460.00	975.00
b	1818	5 D /50 (rev.)	—	—	—	—
S2174	1819	....	51,723	—	3500.	7500.
a	1819	5 D/50 (rev.)	—	—	rare	—
S2175	1820	curved base 2, sm. letters.............	263,806	—	400.00	950.00
a	1820	curved base 2, large letters	—	—	400.00	950.00
b	1820	square base 2..........................	—	—	325.00	850.00
S2180	1825/21	....	29,060	—	850.00	2100.00
S2181	1825/24	....	—	—	RARE	—
S2184	1828/27	....	28,029	—	—	5250.00
S2186	1829	small date.............................	57,442	—	—	2100.00
a	1829	large date.............................	—	—	—	—
S2187	1830	small 5 rev............................	126,351	—	500.00	1800.00
a	1830	large 5 rev............................	—	—	500.00	1800.00
S2189	1832	curved base 2, 12 stars................	157,487	—	—	—
a	1832	square base 2, 13 stars................	—	—	1400.00	4100.00
S2191	1834	plain 4, motto	50,141	—	550.00	1800.00
a	1834	crosslet 4, motto	—	—	675.00	2000.00
S2192	1834	plain 4, no motto	658,000	—	55.00	150.00
a	1834	crosslet 4, no motto	—	—	135.00	450.00
S2200	1839/8	....	118,143	—	RARE	—
S2211	1842	small letters..........................	27,578	—	80.00	225.00
a	1842	large letters	—	—	70.00	165.00
S2212	1842C	small date.............................	27,480	—	125.00	250.00
a	1842C	large date.............................	—	—	135.00	260.00
S2213	1842D	small date.............................	59,608	—	110.00	200.00
a	1842D	large date.............................	—	—	110.00	200.00
S2218	18430	small letters..........................	101,075	—	75.00	105.00

GOLD PIECES

Index #	Date	Description	Mintage	Good	Fine	Unc.
a	18430	large letters	—	—	75.00	105.00
S2228	1846D	double MM	80,294	—	150.00	250.00
S2230	1847		915,900	—	30.00	60.00
a	1847	7/7	—	—	70.00	115.00
b	1847	double 18	—	—	70.00	120.00
c	1847	top of 7 in border	—	—	rare	—
S2338	1880		3,166,436	—	19.00	30.00
a	1880	recut date	—	—	28.00	40.00
S2340	1880S		1,348,900	—	19.00	30.00
a	1880S	large MM	—	—	—	—
b	1880S	small MM	—	—	—	—
c	1880S	various position MM	—	—	—	—
S2243	1851/1		377,505	—	80.00	150.00
S2315	1873	open 3	112,505	—	50.00	75.00
a	1873	closed 3	—	—	70.00	125.00
S2339	1881/1880		5,708,000	—	90.00	155.00
S2342	1882	double profile	2,514,000	—	39.00	60.00
S2356	1887 S/7		1,912,000	—	110.00	170.00
S2391	1902S	double MM	939,000	—	65.00	90.00

$10.00 GOLD PIECES 1795 - 1933

1911
INDIAN
HEAD TYPE

S2430	1797	small eagle	9,177	—	700.00	2500.00
a	1797	large eagle	—	—	500.00	1200.00
S2431	1798/97	9 stars left, 4 right	7,974	—	1200.00	2400.00
a	1798/97	7 stars left, 6 right	—	—	2000.00	7000.00
S2439	1839	small letters	38,248	—	275.00	700.00
a	1839	large letters	—	—	275.00	700.00
S2443	1842	small date	81,507	—	55.00	120.00
a	1842	large date	—	—	55.00	120.00
S2497	1865S	/ inverted 186 ....rare	16,700	—	Rare	—
S2540	1881	double profile	3,877,000	—	60.00	85.00

$20.00 GOLD PIECES 1849-1933

1906
LIBERTY
HEAD TYPE

S2653	1853/2		1,261,326	—	100.00	225.00
S2655	1854	recut date	—	—	90.00	195.00
S2706	1873	open 3	1,709,825	—	200.00	550.00
a	1873	closed 3	—	—	90.00	200.00

GOLD PIECES

Index #	Date	Description	Mintage	Good	Fine	Unc.

1907
ROMAN
NUMERAL
SAINT
GAUDENS
TYPE
(HIGH RELIEF)

Index #	Date	Description	Mintage	Good	Fine	Unc.
S2794	1907	high relief Roman numeral (MCMVII) wire rim	11,250	—	500.00	1000.00
a	1907	same as above flat rim	—	—	500.00	1000.00

1929
WITH
MOTTO
ST. GAUDENS TYPE
(FLAT TYPE)

Index #	Date	Description	Mintage	Good	Fine	Unc.
S2795	1907	Arabic numerals, flat design	361,667	—	49.00	65.00
S2796	1908	no motto	4,271,551	—	49.00	65.00
a	1908	motto	156,359	—	50.00	75.00
S2800	1909		161,282	—	50.00	75.00
a	1909/8		—	—	110.00	150.00
S2802	1909S		2,774,900	—	60.00	85.00
a	1909S	double MM	—	—	75.00	110.00
S2807	1911D		846,000	—	50.00	80.00
a	1911D	double MM	—	—	55.00	85.00

NOTE—1913-1932 all have 48 stars on edge

REFERENCE CHART FOR METAL CHARACTERS

	Melting Point (Fahrenheit)	Hardness (Kilograms per square millimeter)	Specific gravity
Platinum............(Pt.)	3,171°	50	21.5
Gold............(AU)	1,945°	18	19.3
Silver............(Ag)	1,762°	25	10.1
Nickel............(Ni)	2,651°	80	8.9
Copper............(Cu)	1,983°	50	8.9
Iron............(Fe)	2,368°	60	7.8
Aluminum............(Al)	1,216°	18	2.6
Tin............(Sn)	449°	8	7.3
Lead............(Pb)	620°	4	11.4
Zinc............(Zn)	786°	35	7.0

A quick glance will show Nickel is the hardest, Lead the softest, and Platinum the heaviest and most resistant to heat.

PROOF SETS

"FROSTED" GEM 1st STRIKE 1957 PROOF SET

A frosted coin appears to have a milky, grayish or velvet finish.

REGULAR U.S. PROOF SETS

Interest in frosted coins has increased with many proof sets containing one or more coins in a frosted state. Many collectors asked why they are frosted and if there is any extra value realized for them.

Frosted coins in my opinion are worth an added premium. They are the result of first strikes from new dies.

Frosted coins have been listed and advertised as Gem, first strikes, and frosted. If one takes the time he will see that a "frosted coin" is the fleur de coin. The contrast of the frost and the glowing surface adds color and insures the coin was a first strike from a new die, thus the features and lettering will be at their maximum sharpness.

When the die surface wears due to thousands of strokes of use, the incused parts tend to polish through friction and wear. A blank proof is glossy throughout, when they are struck on new dies the tiny rough incused surface will leave the same impression on the coin. New dies have a smooth glossy field, the incused parts such as the features, design and lettering are never polished.

The reason for only the obverse or reverse being frosted is that only one die was changed. Thus the new die will create a frosted effigy.

Proof surface is proper to use, when you consider how a proof is made, you can readily see how some misconceptions come about.

A proof coin is the result of the metal being perfect, clear of blemishes and glossy mirror-like. The pressure required for clear sharp features is many more tons of pressure than used on regular coins. Thus a proof glossy surface blank must be used to get a "proof surface", if an ordinary new blank is used the field surface will be the same as an ordinary uncirculated coin. It is my opinion that many "proof surface" silver dollars were originally (proof blanks) but struck as regular coins under less pressures than proofs are, which accounts for the proof surface, but rounded edges rather than squared as proofs are known.

The collector is constantly dividing and separating the classifications. "Proof surface" will eventually be in a class of its own. There is no difference in the "field appearance" of a Proof or "Proof Surface" coin. There is a difference in the manufacture of a (Proof Coin) — (Proof Surface Coin).

Index #	Date	Description	Mintage	Good	Fine	Unc.

1892-1893 COLUMBIAN EXPOSITION

A commemorative designed by C. E. Barber and G. T. Morgan

1893 COMMEMORATIVE

1892 2 OVER 2

1892 DOUBLE DATE

Index #	Date	Description	Mintage	Good	Fine	Unc.
S2844	1892	....	950,000	—	2.50	7.00
a	1892	1892/2	—	—	6.00	16.00
b	1892	recut date Small/large	—	—	16.50	37.00
c	1892	recut date & lettering	—	—	20.00	50.00
d	1892	dot under world, rev. very scarce.............	—	—	35.00	65.00
e	1892	clog side of 8 recut 9............................	—	—	6.00	17.00
f	1892	recut 892	—	—	7.00	20.00
g	1892	recut date, shifted East	—	—	16.00	40.00
h	1892	recut date, shifted West, letters of Worlds shifted South, Columbian & Chicago to the West...................	—	—	21.00	55.00
i	1892	Recut date shifted East, recut or repunched 2/2 top edge South, very scarce.................	—	—	37.00	65.00
j	1892	recut date, letters & repunched 92/92 very rare	—	—	50.00	95.00
k	1892	recut date..	(Proof)	very scarce		125.00
l	1892	recut date & lettering	(Proof)	very scarce		140.00
m	1892	die break thru top of word Worlds......	—	—	2.50	8.50
n	1892	die break thru top of word Columbian......	—	—	2.50	8.50
o	1892	light recut date..................................	—	—	8.00	20.00
p	1892	Jaggered die break thru bottom of date ...	—	—	2.50	10.00
q	1892	recut 92	—	—	6.00	16.00
r	1892	recut date heavy to the North, recut letters of Worlds & Columbian to the West	—	—	18.00	37.00
s	1892	recut date, die break thru Chicago, recut word Exposition, recut 9	—	—	6.00	17.00
t	1892	recut small/large date, recut World's South, Columbian to the East, Die br. over Chicago with recut 0, recut Exposition..	—	—	18.00	40.00
	1892	....				
u	1892	L design rudder..................................	—	—	—	—
v	1892	plain design rudder.............................	—	—	—	—

105

COMMEMORATIVE HALF DOLLARS

Index #	Date	Description	Mintage	Good	Fine	Unc.

1893
DOUBLE
DATE

1893
3 OVER 3

Index #	Date	Description	Mintage	Good	Fine	Unc.
2845	1893	....	1,550,405	—	1.00	4.75
a	1893	recut date	(Proof)	very scarce		95.00
b	1893	Recut date all kinds......................	—	—	5.50	25.00
c	1893	recut date shifted East, recut let. Chicago to West................................	—	—	7.50	30.00
d	1893	Recut date & Chicago shifted West, Columbian to South........................	—	—	7.50	30.00

DOUBLE
LETTERING
ON WORLDS

CHICAGO
DOUBLE
LETTERING

Index #	Date	Description	Mintage	Good	Fine	Unc.
e	1893	light recut date............................	—	—	3.00	10.00
f	1893	recut 9	—	—	2.00	8.00
g	1893	recut 893	—	—	2.75	9.00
h	1893	recut 93	—	—	2.75	9.00
i	1893	3/3..	—	—	2.75	9.00
j	1893	clog side of 8 recut 93	—			
k	1893	engraving, E. Joslin, Whitehall, N.Y. in field of obverse. Rev. in the mast of ship, the date 4/28/97 unattributed........		Rare		
l	1893	White metal, 5 grains heavier than reg. issue unattributed		Rare		

DOUBLE DATE
AND
LETTERING

DIEBREAK
THROUGH
WORLD

Index #	Date	Description	Mintage	Good	Fine	Unc.
m	1893	plain edge	—	—	—	—
n	1893	part broken rudder........................	—	—	—	—
o	1893	part broken rudder, right upper deck has broken rails	—	—	—	—
p	1893	clash dies......................................	—	—	—	—

1925 STONE MOUNTAIN MEMORIAL

Designed by Gutzon Borglum

STONE MOUNTAIN
WITH
DESIGNER'S
INITIAL

Index #	Date	Description	Mintage	Good	Fine	Unc.
2858	1925	....	1,314,709	—	2.75	9.00
a	1925	double date all kinds	—	—	8.00	15.00
b	1925	double date & lettering, Stone Mountain	—	—	10.00	25.00

DOUBLE, TRIPLE AND MULTIPLE STRUCK COINS

Date	Description	Mintage	Good	Fine	Unc.

This occurs when the release mechanism fails to ·eject the first strike. Double strikes with two different dates are probably caused by an earlier date coin finding its way into the press while a later date is being struck. Note, beware of double struck coins that are made outside of the mints, especially incused double strikes. These can be easily made by pressing two coins together in a vise. A genuine brockage will show only one incused impression.

1893 TRIPLE STRUCK INDIAN CENT

1911P DOUBLE STRUCK LINCOLN CENT

OBVERSE

REVERSE

Date	Description	Mintage	Good	Fine	Unc.
1893	Triple struck Indian cent	—	—	—	—
1910P	Triple Struck	—	36.00	67.50	110.00
1911P	double struck obv.-rev.	—	16.25	47.50	100.00
1914P	Double Struck	—	36.00	62.50	95.00

1915 D LINCOLN DOUBLE STRUCK

OBVERSE

REVERSE

Date	Description	Mintage	Good	Fine	Unc.
1915D	Double Struck	—	36.00	62.50	95.00
1916P	Double Struck	—	31.00	57.50	90.00
1916D	Double Struck	—	36.00	67.50	105.00
1917P	Multi Struck				
1918D	Double Struck	—	31.00	67.50	90.00
1918S	Double Struck	—	36.00	67.50	100.00

1921 S LINCOLN DOUBLE STRUCK

OBVERSE

REVERSE

1924P DOUBLE STRUCK

Date	Description	Mintage	Good	Fine	Unc.
1921S	Double Struck	—	46.00	82.50	145.00
1921P	1921/1920 P	—	51.00	87.50	115.00
1924P	Double Struck	—	36.00	77.50	105.00
1924S	Double Struck	—	51.00	97.50	155.00
1926D	Double Struck	—	41.00	67.50	100.00
1927P	Double Struck	—	61.00	97.50	130.00
1931D	Double Struck	—	51.00	87.50	105.00
1933D	Double Struck	—	51.00	87.50	115.00
1935P	Double Struck	—	36.00	67.50	90.00

DOUBLE, TRIPLE AND MULTIPLE STRUCK COINS

Date	Description	Mintage	Good	Fine	Unc.

1937 LINCOLN DOUBLE STRUCK

OBVERSE   REVERSE

Date	Description	Mintage	Good	Fine	Unc.
1937P	Double Struck	—	35.00	65.00	104.50
1937/1935	Double struck obv.	—	35.00	75.00	220.00
1939P	Triple Struck	—	35.00	85.00	110.00
1939P	Double Struck	—	35.00	65.00	93.50
1940D	Double Struck	—	35.00	60.00	104.50
1944P	Double Struck	—	35.00	65.00	93.50
1945S	Double Struck	—	35.00	65.00	93.50
1945D	Double Struck	—	35.00	65.00	93.50
1945P	1945/1944	—	50.00	85.00	121.00

1948 P DOUBLE STRUCK

OBVERSE   REVERSE

Date	Description	Mintage	Good	Fine	Unc.
1945P	Double Struck	—	35.00	65.00	93.50
1946S	Double Struck	—	35.00	65.00	93.50
1946D	Double Struck	—	35.00	65.00	93.50
1947D	Double Struck	—	35.00	65.00	93.50
1947P	Double Struck	—	35.00	65.00	93.50
1948P	Double Struck	—	35.00	65.00	93.50
1948P	1948/1946	—	50.00	85.00	121.00
1949P	Multi Struck	—	38.00	70.00	104.50
1949P	multiple struck	—	45.00	95.00	220.00
1950P	1950/48	—	38.00	70.00	104.50
1950D	Double Struck	—	35.00	65.00	93.50
1951P	Double Struck	—	35.00	65.00	93.50
1951P	Triple Struck	—	35.00	65.00	93.50
1952P	Double Struck	—	35.00	65.00	93.50
1953P	Double Struck	—	50.00	85.00	121.00
1954S	Double Struck	—	40.00	70.00	110.00
1954P	Double Struck	—	35.00	65.00	93.50

1955 D DOUBLE STRUCK

OBVERSE   REVERSE

1955D DOUBLE STRUCK

Date	Description	Mintage	Good	Fine	Unc.
1955D	Double Struck	—	40.00	70.00	110.00
1955P	Double Struck	—	38.00	80.00	137.50

DOUBLE, TRIPLE AND MULTIPLE STRUCK COINS

Date	Description	Mintage	Good	Fine	Unc.
1956P	Multi Struck	—	35.00	65.00	93.50
1956D	Double Struck	—	35.00	65.00	93.50
1957D	Double Struck	—	50.00	85.00	121.00
1957P	1957/1944	—	50.00	85.00	121.00
1958D	Double Struck	—	38.00	70.00	104.50
1959D	1959D/1958	—	40.00	70.00	104.50
1959P	Triple Struck	—	35.00	65.00	93.50
1959D	Double Struck	—	45.00	70.00	104.50

1960 D OVER 59 D LINCOLN

OBVERSE   REVERSE

Date	Description	Mintage	Good	Fine	Unc.
1960D	1960/1959	—	50.00	75.00	121.00
1960D	sm. date double struck ODV.-rev.	—	—	—	110.00
1961P	double struck OBV.-Rev	—	—	50.00	106.70
1961P	1961/1960 D Double Struck	—	35.00	65.00	93.50
1961P	Double Struck	—	50.00	75.00	121.00
1961P	1961/1960 Triple Struck	—	35.00	65.00	93.50
1961D	3 dates, Multiple Struck	—	—	65.00	105.00
1961D	double struck, obverse & reverse	—	—	50.00	104.50
1961D	1961/1960 Multi Struck	—	35.00	65.00	93.50

1961 D DOUBLE STRUCK OBVERSE AND REVERSE 180° ROTATED STAMPED

1961 D DOUBLE STRUCK

Date	Description	Mintage	Good	Fine	Unc.
1961D	Double Struck	—	50.00	75.00	121.00
1962D	Double Struck	—	60.00	85.00	132.00

1962 D DOUBLE STRUCK

OBVERSE

REVERSE

1962P DOUBLE STRUCK

Date	Description	Mintage	Good	Fine	Unc.
1962D	1962/1961 D Triple	—	35.00	65.00	93.50
1962D	1962/1961 D Multi	—	35.00	65.00	93.50

1944 LINCOLN (Poorly Annealed)
Double impression cents as above are referred to as wavy or rippled. This is not the result of a double strike or die defect but the result of the annealing heat process. The coin if not properly cooled, will create a flowing effect on the surface and designs. Values are dependent on the oddity, appearance and collector's demand.

(FIG. A)

**1955
DOUBLE HEAD
RAISED OBVERSE
INCUSED REVERSE**

Brockage errors are another interesting series to collect, these exist in early U.S. and foreign coins. What is a brockage? This is a term given to coins impressed by another while in the press.

Visualize a blank being struck and sticking to the bottom die, the obverse will be facing up, the next blank coming in lays on top of the already struck coin. The press strikes again leaving the obverse of the 1st coin impressed in the back of the top coin (incused) resulting in figure (A). The opposite holds true if the blank sticks to the upper die thus two tails or reverses as in figure (B).

It is hardly likely two coins will be stuck to both the upper and lower dies, however, if it is possible, there will be two incused impressions, an obverse and a reverse, a truly prized error.

A more complicated error would be a brockage sticking to the upper die receiving the impression of the obverse (impressed) then free itself to rest on the bottom die and receive another strike. The result, an incused obverse with a raised reverse, and a possible double impression of the obverse or top side.

**1808
LARGE
CENT**

INCUSED

REVERSE

**REVERSE
NORMAL
RAISED**

(FIG. B)

Resulted when struck blank is not ejected and a blank is restruck on finished coin causing metal feathers to spread.

OFF METAL PLANCHETS

Off metal coins result from a mix up of blank planchets getting into a press hopper and being struck on a coin of another denomination, or the changing of dies for a new issue while some blanks still remain in the hopper.

The following list is compiled from known listings, collections, exhibits and auction catalogs.

Values are dependent on the supply, demand, oddity and what the market will bear. There is no set or standard values.

VALUES RANGE FROM $35.00 AND UP

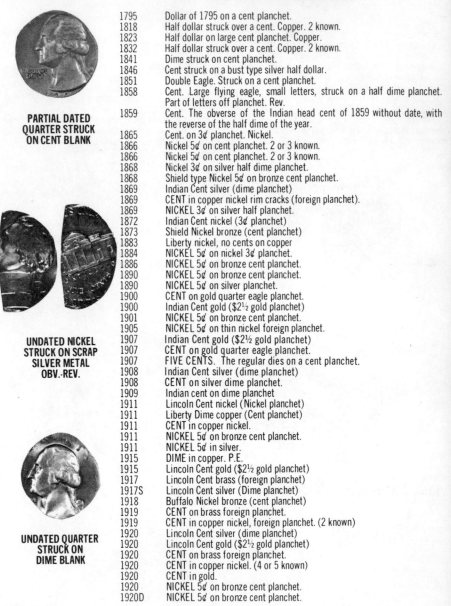

PARTIAL DATED QUARTER STRUCK ON CENT BLANK

UNDATED NICKEL STRUCK ON SCRAP SILVER METAL OBV.-REV.

UNDATED QUARTER STRUCK ON DIME BLANK

1795	Dollar of 1795 on a cent planchet.
1818	Half dollar struck over a cent. Copper. 2 known.
1823	Half dollar on large cent planchet. Copper.
1832	Half dollar struck over a cent. Copper. 2 known.
1841	Dime struck on cent planchet.
1846	Cent struck on a bust type silver half dollar.
1851	Double Eagle. Struck on a cent planchet.
1858	Cent. Large flying eagle, small letters, struck on a half dime planchet. Part of letters off planchet. Rev.
1859	Cent. The obverse of the Indian head cent of 1859 without date, with the reverse of the half dime of the year.
1865	Cent. on 3¢ planchet. Nickel.
1866	Nickel 5¢ on cent planchet. 2 or 3 known.
1866	Nickel 5¢ on cent planchet. 2 or 3 known.
1868	Nickel 3¢ on silver half dime planchet.
1868	Shield type Nickel 5¢ on bronze cent planchet.
1869	Indian Cent silver (dime planchet)
1869	CENT in copper nickel rim cracks (foreign planchet).
1869	NICKEL 3¢ on silver half planchet.
1872	Indian Cent nickel (3¢ planchet)
1873	Shield Nickel bronze (cent planchet)
1883	Liberty nickel, no cents on copper
1884	NICKEL 5¢ on nickel 3¢ planchet.
1886	NICKEL 5¢ on bronze cent planchet.
1890	NICKEL 5¢ on bronze cent planchet.
1890	NICKEL 5¢ on silver planchet.
1900	CENT on gold quarter eagle planchet.
1900	Indian Cent gold ($2½ gold planchet)
1901	NICKEL 5¢ on bronze cent planchet.
1905	NICKEL 5¢ on thin nickel foreign planchet.
1907	Indian Cent gold ($2½ gold planchet)
1907	CENT on gold quarter eagle planchet.
1907	FIVE CENTS. The regular dies on a cent planchet.
1908	Indian Cent silver (dime planchet)
1908	CENT on silver dime planchet.
1909	Indian cent on dime planchet
1911	Lincoln Cent nickel (Nickel planchet)
1911	Liberty Dime copper (Cent planchet)
1911	CENT in copper nickel.
1911	NICKEL 5¢ on bronze cent planchet.
1911	NICKEL 5¢ in silver.
1915	DIME in copper. P.E.
1915	Lincoln Cent gold ($2½ gold planchet)
1917	Lincoln Cent brass (foreign planchet)
1917S	Lincoln Cent silver (Dime planchet)
1918	Buffalo Nickel bronze (cent planchet)
1919	CENT on brass foreign planchet.
1919	CENT in copper nickel, foreign planchet. (2 known)
1920	Lincoln Cent silver (dime planchet)
1920	Lincoln Cent gold ($2½ gold planchet)
1920	CENT on brass foreign planchet.
1920	CENT in copper nickel. (4 or 5 known)
1920	CENT in gold.
1920	NICKEL 5¢ on bronze cent planchet.
1920D	NICKEL 5¢ on bronze cent planchet.

OFF METAL PLANCHETS

**1942 HALF STRUCK
ON QUARTER**

**1943S CENT
STRUCK ON DIME**

**1962 HALF DOLLAR
ON QUARTER**

1920	NICKEL 5¢ on silver dime planchet.
1920S	NICKEL 5¢ in copper.
1920	QUARTER DOLLAR on nickel foreign planchet.
1924	NICKEL 5¢ on cent planchet.
1925	CENT in silver.
1925S	CENT on silver dime planchet.
1928	CENT on silver dime planchet.
1929	NICKEL 5¢ on silver dime planchet.
1934	NICKEL 5¢ on bronze cent planchet.
1935	Washington 25¢ bronze (cent planchet)
1938	NICKEL 5¢ on bronze cent planchet.
1939	Jefferson 5¢ bronze (foreign planchet)
1939S	NICKEL 5¢ on silver dime planchet.
1939	QUARTER DOLLAR in nickel.
1939	QUARTER on nickel.
1940	CENT on silver dime planchet.
1940	CENT on brass foreign planchet.
1941	CENT on brass foreign planchet.
1941S	CENT on brass foreign planchet.
1941	CENT on silver dime planchet.
1941	CENT in silver (full planchet).
1941D	CENT on silver dime planchet.
1941	NICKEL 5¢ on bronze cent planchet. Also on Lincoln cent.
1941	NICKEL 5¢ on silver dime planchet.
1941S	NICKEL 5¢ on silver dime planchet.
1941	QUARTER DOLLAR on bronze cent planchet.
1942	Lincoln Cent brass (foreign planchet).
1942	CENT in white metal.
1942	CENT on silver.
1942S	NICKEL 5¢ on silver dime planchet.
1943	Lincoln Cent silver (dime planchet).
1943D	CENT on silver dime planchet.
1943S	CENT on silver dime planchet.
1943	NICKEL 5¢ on steel & zinc cent planchet.
1943S	NICKEL 5¢ on steel & zinc cent planchet.
1943S	NICKEL 5¢ on aluminum-bronze foreign planchet.
1943	QUARTER DOLLAR on aluminum-bronze foreign planchet.
1944	Lincoln Cents steel (previous year planchet).
1944	Jefferson 5¢ bronze (cent planchet).
1944	CENT on aluminum-bronze foreign planchet.
1944	CENT on silver dime planchet.
1944	CENT in silver planchet.
1944	CENT on brass foreign planchet.
1944D	CENT on silver dime planchet.
1944	NICKEL 5¢ on silver dime planchet.
1944	NICKEL 5¢ on steel & zinc planchet.
1944	QUARTER DOLLAR on steel & zinc cent planchet.
1945S	CENT on Roosevelt dime.
1945	CENT in silver.
1945	NICKEL 5¢ on silver dime planchet.
1945S	NICKEL 5¢ on silver dime planchet.
1946	CENT on silver dime planchet.
1946S	CENT on silver dime planchet.
1946	NICKEL 5¢ on bronze cent planchet.
1946S	Washington 25¢ silver (dime planchet).
1947S	CENT on silver.
1949	DIME on small silver foreign planchet.
1949	QUARTER DOLLAR on nickel 5¢ planchet.
1950	Lincoln Cent silver (dime planchet).
1950D	CENT on silver dime planchet.
1950	NICKEL 5¢ on silver dime planchet.
1951D	Lincoln Cent silver (dime planchet).
1951D	CENT on silver dime planchet.
1951S	CENT on silver dime planchet.
1951D	NICKEL 5¢ on silver dime planchet.

MISCELLANEOUS ODD COINS

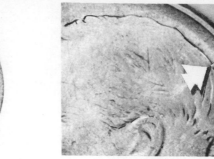

ROOSEVELT HORNED HEAD

1962 D LINCOLN CRUDED EDGE
NO COLLAR

1st OPERATION BLANK PLANCHET (FLAT EDGE)

2nd OPERATION BLANK PLANCHET (UPSET EDGE)

LINCOLN WITH REVERSE
SHOWING THROUGH OBVERSE

1946 ROOSEVELT DIME WITH
PEELED LAMINATION SHELL

OFF CENTERED PLANCHET GAUGE

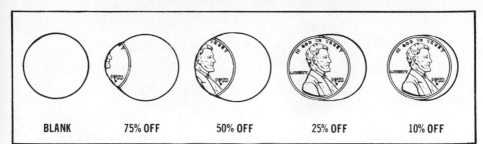

| BLANK | 75% OFF | 50% OFF | 25% OFF | 10% OFF |

CLIPPED PLANCHET GAUGE

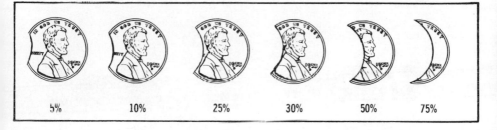

| 5% | 10% | 25% | 30% | 50% | 75% |

ROTATED DIE GAUGE

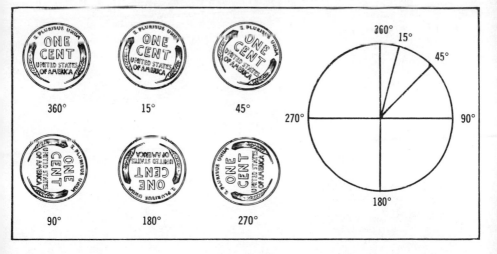

The above illustrations are gauges to help the collector to determine the various positions of the three popular series. They are off center, clipped planchets, and rotated dies. A rather interesting, unique and colorful collection of these oddities can be assembled. They always make an interesting display. Values are determined by supply and demand, and what the market will bear.

PATTERNS AND TRIAL PIECES

1882 LIBERTY HEAD NICKEL PATTERN

This design was accepted by the act of congress. The regular minting of this issue started in 1883 of which 5,479,519 pieces were struck without the word cents at the reverse side. Later a second issue was struck of 16,032,983 with the word cents. From then on all Liberty Head nickels have the word CENTS on the reverse.

This 1882 pattern is known to have been struck in Nickel, Bronze, and Aluminum.

All patterns are struck in proof in other metals to test for sharpness of impression and acceptance of de·signs submitted by several designers and engravers—to Congressional Committee for approval.

REJECTED
DESIGN OF
PATTERN FOR
1882 LIBERTY
NICKEL

REJECTED PATTERN
1876 BRONZE PATTERN DOLLAR

Abbreviations Used
with U. S. Coins

Engravers' Initials

AF—Anthony De Francisci
AW—A. A. Weinman
B—Charles E. Barber
C. Gobrecht—Christian Gobrecht
F—James E. Fraser
FG—Frank Gasparro
FS—Felix Schlag
GR—Gilroy Roberts
JF—John Flanagan
JS—John R. Sinnock
L—James Longacre
M—Herman A. MacNeil
M—George T. Morgan
VDB—Victor David Brenner

Mint Marks

C—Charlotte, N. C.
CC—Carson City, Nevada
D—Dahlonega, Georgia
D—Denver, Colo.
O—New Orleans, La.
P—Philadelphia
S—San Francisco, Calif.

OFF CENTERED PLANCHETS

Values of this type error is dependent on the oddity and extremity of the error. Prices shown are for average condition, choice unc. are worth more. This error results when part of the blank is on the die.

1829 Large cent, obv.-rev.. $55.00
   no date large cent obv.-rev... 60.00

1862 copper nickel cent, obv.-rev................................... 40.00
1863 copper nickel cent, obv. .... —
1963 cent, rare, end of strip edge blank............................. —

1901 Indian cent, obv.. 35.00
1902 Indian cent, obv.. 35.00
1903 Indian cent. obv.. 35.00

1943 steel   1943 copper

no date, quarter struck on dime planchet,
   rev... 85.00
1943 copper cent, rare .... RARE
1943 steel cent,.. 45.00
1951S cent 5.00

117

OFF CENTERED PLANCHETS

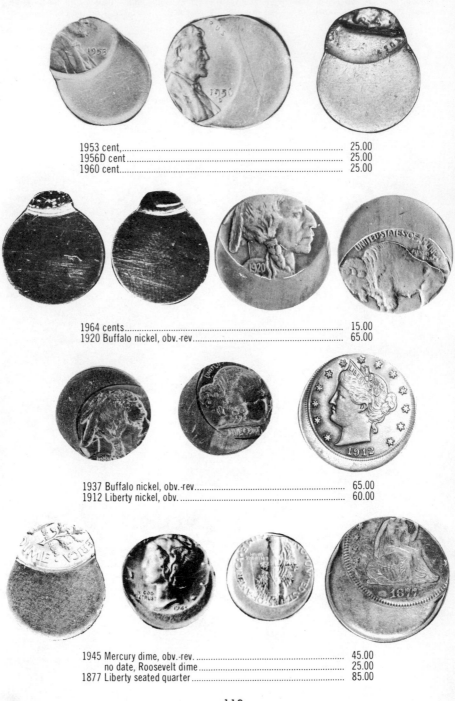

1953 cent,... 25.00
1956D cent.. 25.00
1960 cent.. 25.00

1964 cents... 15.00
1920 Buffalo nickel, obv.-rev.................................... 65.00

1937 Buffalo nickel, obv.-rev.................................... 65.00
1912 Liberty nickel, obv. 60.00

1945 Mercury dime, obv.-rev. 45.00
     no date, Roosevelt dime................................... 25.00
1877 Liberty seated quarter...................................... 85.00

OFF CENTERED DOUBLE STRUCK COINS

This type error happens when the blank is struck with the first impression and receives a second strike while partly ejected. Choice and uncirculated pieces are worth more.

1888 Indian cent, obv.-rev. 150.00

1893 Indian cent, obv. rare, clipped, and double struck
    off centered 225.00
1896 Indian cent, obv.-rev. 150.00

1899 Indian cent, obv. 55.00
1902 Indian cent, obv.-rev., obv. elongated, rare 325.00

1907 Indian cent, obv.-rev., weak obv. 125.00
    no date Lincoln cent, obv.-rev. 125.00

119

MISCELLANEOUS ODD COINS

1957 REVERSE STRUCK OVER OBVERSE

ROOSEVELT FANGED DIME

1960 ROOSEVELT DOUBLE STRUCK

ROOSEVELT DIME WITH DIEBREAK THROUGH A

1944 LINCOLN "V"

1961 LINCOLN REED EDGE

1863 CIVIL WAR TOKEN WITH RECUT 3

1960 SMALL DATE PROOF SET 2 DIMES (NO NICKEL)

1961 D LINCOLN WITH PEELED LAMINATED D

MISCELLANEOUS ODD COINS

"ROPE" ERROR
NICKEL

DOLLAR
DIEBREAK IN 1st 8

1948 LAMINATION
PEELING TYPE
CENT

DOUBLE STRUCK
1701 COLONIAL CENT

1955
SCRAP PLANCHET CENT

STAPLE
EMBEDDED TYPE
NICKEL

1946

1956D

PAPER THIN CENTS
(BEWARE OF ACID TREATED)

UNC. 1931S 5¢
WITH BAR EDGE
CLIPPED PLANCHET

FILLED DIE
FIVE CENTS

FILLED DATE
FIVE CENTS

1960-D JEFFERSON

1. EXTENDED RIM EDGE-BAR OF METAL.
2. LIBERTY-BAR "B"
3. LIBERTY-BAR "E"
4. LIBERTY-BAR "R"
5. LIBERTY-BAR "T"
6. DATE-METAL OVER "9"
7. DATE-BAR "6"
8. DATE-BAR ON TOP OF UPPER PART "ZERO"
9. EXTENDED RIM EDGE-BAR OF METAL.
10. SHOULDER OF COAT-DOT OF METAL.

11. "GOD"-FILLED LOWER PORTION "G".
12. "GOD"-FILLED LOWER PORTION "O".
13. "GOD"-FILLED LOWER PORTION "D".
14. "WE"-LEFT LOWER "E" METAL EXTENSION. ADDITIONALLY BETWEEN "1" AND "9".

RIM IS LINED OR GROOVED. SOME FROSTING ON COIN. UNDER PART OF CHIN IS ROUGH. CONDITION-PU-BAG MARKED.

CLIPPED PLANCHETS

This is a common error occurring among coins, the photos shown here are only a small example of what may be found. To list and value all kinds would require a separate catalog.

The error is caused at the blanking stage where a blank is partly in or out of the slot, and the cutting edge of the die shears or dips the part lying outside of the die. This can also happen if a coin fails to eject fully after being struck.

Values depend on the type error and the oddity of it and of course, the condition of coin.

**ROOSEVELT DIME
DOUBLE CLIP
PLANCHET**

1864 Copper nickel Indian cent.................$8.00
1959 Lincoln cent, top clip .... .75
1959 Lincoln cent, half moon 1.25
Roosevelt dime, double clip, spread
cup type...15.00

**1864 C.N.
CLIPPED PLANCHET**

1959 LINCOLN CLIP CENT

**1959 LINCOLN
1/3 CLIP PLANCHET**

CLASHED DIE VARIETY

Clashed die varieties exist in many type coins mainly early dates, such as bust type halves, large cents and one dollar gold type 3. The cause of this variety happens when the obverse and reverse dies clash together without a metal blank between them. Both dies have incused impressions which have sharp edges that cut in to each other, thus impressions are left on the surface notably in the field. The process is the same as oinking a new working die. When this happens to a pair of dies most all coins struck from them will show the impression.

All working coin presses have adjustments of pressure according to the type metal used and impression feature desired. When the new dies are set in the press, they are aligned and adjusted. It's at this point when the variety can occur. The press can be over pressured by too much downward pressure and if the press is operated accidently the dies clash thus leaving impressions.

ROTATED REVERSE DIE SHIFTS

Rotated dies are listed as clockwise. Its' possible to have a rotated shift counter clockwise, but there is no way of being sure of the shift direction.

1798	large cent 90°	1864L	cent 180°	1920D	dime 320°	
1809	half cent 160°	1865	Rotated Rev die shift 90°	1923P	silver dollar 90°	
1816	cent 310°	1869	cent 180°	1924D	cent 10° 35° 45° 60°	
1829	cent 15°	1878CC	45° 180°		180° 240°	
1836	dime 30°	18830	45° 90°	1926D	cent 345°	
1849	half cent 90°	18910	silver dollar 170°	1930P	buffalo nickel 60°	
1854	cent 90°	18990	silver dollar 45° 90°	1960D	dime 20°	
1864	Two cent 15° 35° 60° 90° 170° 180° 245° 270° 360°					

1883 LIBERTY NICKEL WITH DIE BREAKS

1964 KENNEDY HALF, WITH PLANCHET DEFECT

1957 ROOSEVELT DIME WITH WART OVER EYE

MISCELLANEOUS ODD COINS

1959 LIBERTY BUBBLED METAL

CALIFORNIA IMITATION GOLD
TOKEN—OFF CENTER STRUCK

FLYING EAGLE 1/10 MIL CENT

1796 SILVER DOLLAR
SMALL DATE

1796 SILVER DOLLAR (REVERSE)
SMALL EAGLE

1837 FEUCHTWANGER CENT GERMAN SILVER (TRIAL PIECE)

1863 CIVIL WAR CENT TOKEN

"If anybody attempts to tear it down, shoot him on the spot" quotation refers to the United States flag.

RARE 1849 MASSACHUSETTS - CALIFORNIA CO. FIVE DOLLAR GOLD: ALSO KNOWN TO BE STRUCK IN NICKEL ALLOY

Additional Books for the Collector
FROM ANCO

Detecting Altered Coins

by Bert Harsche

Whether you are a collector, dealer or investor this book is an absolute must for your library.

Contained in its 28 pages is valuable information, with accompanying photographs, on how to detect numerous coin forgeries. Altered 1909-s V.D.B., 1864-L Indian and 1914-D Lincolns are just a few of the more popular coins covered.

A must for your library, Detecting Altered Coins sells for $1.00.

North American Currency

by Grover C. Criswell

North American Currency ranges from colonial issues through broken bank notes to state and national currency with sections on Canada and Mexico. Over 2,188 different items are illustrated in this big 912 page book.

This volume is the result of 15 years of research in dealing and collecting of paper money by the author. North American Currency is perhaps as comprehensive a coverage of this fascinating subject as can be expected. Available for $15.00.

Confederate and Southern States Bonds

by Grover C. Criswell

Confederate and Southern States Bonds is a companion volume to the Confederate and Southern States Currency book.

It contains over 310 pages and hundreds of illustrations of Confederate and Southern States Bonds, there are 5 pages in color! This volume is the first complete listing since 1876 of the various types of fiscal paper issued by the Confederacy, and the ONLY complete listing of Confederate Bonds.

A handsome addition to any collector's library. Priced at $10.00, which includes price list and supplement.

Medallic Portraits of John F. Kennedy

by Edward C. Rochette

Medallic Portraits of John F. Kennedy . . . and illustrated catalog of the coins, medals and tokens issued in honor of the late president.

More than 600 varieties are listed with a brief history of each issue. A relative valuation guide is included, as well as a practical numbering system.

The book has been published in two editions to give all collectors the opportunity to own Medallic Portraits of John F. Kennedy. A paperback edition, only $2.95, and a beautifully bound library edition is available for $4.95.

Guiton's Coin Grading Guide

by Harold H. Guiton

Carefully detailed descriptions, accompanied by appropriately pin-pointed coin photographs, provide the beginning and advanced collector with an authoritative guide to the grading of United States coins. Covered in the volume are all minor, silver and gold regular issue coins, from half cents through double eagles, issued since 1793.

Full descriptions of the degree of wear on both the obverse and reverse of each type are individually provided for eight conditions ranging from uncirculated to about good. Containing 105 pages of invaluable grading information for the collector of United States coins, this volume is attractively priced at only $1.95.

Confederate and Southern States Currency

by Grover C. Criswell

In this handsome bookshelf library edition the author has listed over 1300 Confederate and Southern state notes. Every note listed is priced up to date.

Confederate and Southern States Currency is printed on 8½ x 11 high gloss stock. 415 superbly detailed illustrations are contained in its 280 descriptive pages.

This book is a standard reference for historians, dealers and collectors of Confederate and Southern states notes. Cost of this invaluable guide is $8.95.

Penny Whimsy

by Dr. William S. Sheldon

In Penny Whimsy the author tells you the history of the "Large Cents."

Here in these historic coppers, in that wonderful numismatic period of 1793 to 1814 covered by Penny Whimsy one recalls, feels and relives the stormy but glorious past.

This is a big book in more ways than one. It has 413 pages, packed with history and facts excitingly told. There are 51 plates containing over 400 individual illustrations. Available for $10.00.

Chinese Currency

by Frederick Schjoth

This excellent volume on the coinage of China has been completely revised by Virgil Hancock. It is a big handsome 272 page book containing hundreds of beautiful line drawings and plates.

Among the extremely interesting facts you will learn is the illustrated history of how Chinese characters are formed and what they mean . . . how to read dates on Chinese coins.

A new price supplement is included free with each book.

Chinese Currency is a LIMITED EDITION, available for $12.50.

Coins Questions and Answers

produced by Coins Magazine

Questions and Answers with 128 pages, 250 questions and 90 photographs is comprehensive . . . the only book available which answers full the most frequently asked questions about coins.

Coin descriptions, conditions . . . Collectors organizations . . . Books . . . Early American coins with general information . . . Cents from 1856 . . . Nickels from 1866 . . . Paper Money . . . Medals . . . and tokens are just a partial list of the contents of this book. Price only $1.00.

Now In Production

by Raymond Hu

This book will prove to be an invaluable price guide and reference catalog to the collector of Chinese coins.

All titles available from your favorite dealer.

INDEX